Praise for

The Well-Being Bucket List
29 Mindful Choices for Older Adults

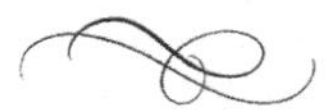

"It is rare to read something that, in plain language, blends a no-holds-barred look at the real challenges of living in the world today, with the pragmatic and Spiritual opportunities available to salve them. This is a must-read book for anyone seeking greater well-being in their life—all of us. Among many terrific dialogues, Steve and Will's conversations on "Remembering the Light Within" and "Surviving Death" are not to be missed."

~ **Dr. Ron Hulnick,** President, University of Santa Monica

"In a series of compelling, authentic, and engaging conversations, Steve Chandler and William Keiper invite, chide, encourage and challenge you to make your moments count. Empowering and transformational, each chapter concludes with a mindful choice to help you thrive during this part of life. This book beckons you to fully awaken—to the joy of self-discovery, the connection with present-moment awareness, the awe of unapologetic inspiration, and the celebration of your limitless opportunity to create your life as a masterpiece!"

~ **Dr. Pam Garcy,** author of *The Power of Inner Guidance*

"The conversational style between the authors as they present their 29 mindful choices, is a rich mix of facts, thoughts, and wisdom. As we get older it can get easier to shrink our world. This book is the antidote, giving us permission to pay less attention to numerical age and focus more on what you want to do."

~ **Steve Nicol,** co-author with Emma Thomson of *Live a Happy Midlife*

"This is a great book, not only for those entering their senior years, but for anyone at any age who wants to learn how to live life fully, gracefully and without regrets. For those who know the authors, they know that they live their words, and it shows."

~ **Ankush Jain,** author of *Sweet Sharing: Rediscovering the Real You*

"*The Well-Being Bucket List* is filled with wisdom, humor, practical tips, and mindset challenges that come from life experience combined with inspiration. Steve and Will's perspectives are not always the same, but are aligned and provide depth of thought that enables us to dive into our own self-awareness, expand our thinking with a great use of data and research, and open our hearts with a theme of unconditional loving that is digestible and real. Their conversations led me to an unexpected next level of transformation as the book built up to a surprising and inspiring conclusion. I truly feel a heightened sense of well-being having read it. I loved *The Well-Being Bucket List*."

~ **Mark Samuel**, CEO of IMPAQ and author of *The Missing Piece: Reimagining Teambuilding to Achieve Breakthrough Results*

"This book is a conversation between two great minds. The authors convey a method of transformation that is practical and vital. Living longer does nothing for me, if the quality of my time on this earth is not textured with presence, purpose and inspiration. As Thoreau shared with us, many people live lives of "quiet desperation," and this book offers antidotes from the physical to the spiritual realms. As a practitioner of well-being, I recommend "listening in" to Steve and Will's conversations and savoring their wit and wisdom as you consider mindful choices for creating your future."

~ **Stephen McGhee**, founder L4 Initiative (Light, Leadership, Longevity and Life), and founder of McGheeLeadership.com

"In this excellent, collaborative conversation, Chandler and Keiper combine research-based facts on aging, real life experiences and continual reminders of our human, creative power to learn and grow. They empower us through providing practical, mindful choices that can make the difference between languishing in our later years or BEING the vibrant, full expression of who and what we really are! An excellent, life-affirming conversation we all need to be a part of!"

~ **Melissa Ford,** author of *Living Service: The Journey of a Prosperous Coach*

"What I love about the book is that it merges form with philosophy, tools with neuroscience, medicine with mystery, and practicality with spirituality in a way that is useful and profoundly impactful. As for me, my intention is to move forward past the invisible boundary I have named "old" with a vitality and vision that is now more animated by fresh thinking, clearer vision, and a heightened anticipation of what lies round the bend."

~ **Carla Rotering, M.D.**

The Well-Being Bucket List

To Tina and John —
with love —
Steve

29 MINDFUL CHOICES FOR OLDER ADULTS

The Well-Being Bucket List

STEVE CHANDLER & WILLIAM KEIPER

The Well-Being Bucket List: 29 Mindful Choices for Older Adults

Chris Nelson, Editor
Kathy Eimers, Editor
Brannan Sirratt, Editorial Contributor
Carrie Brito, Cover Layout

Imprint: FirstGlobal® Media LLC contact:
publisher@firstglobal.media
Steve Chandler contact: www.stevechandler.com
William Keiper contact: www.williamkeiper.com

Library of Congress Control Number: 2021914537
ISBN: 978-0-9913835-7-3
First Edition

Cover photo: Comstock via Getty (Stockbyte)

You can’t go back and change
the beginning, but you can
start where you are and
change the ending.

~ C. S. Lewis

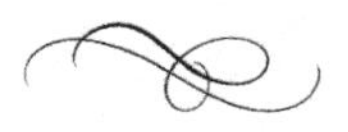

Table of Contents

The Well-Being Bucket List

Conversation Starter
Begin Here

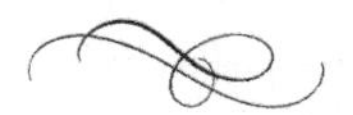

Will

The "bucket list" concept was brought to front-and-center with the 2007 release of *The Bucket List*, starring Jack Nicholson and Morgan Freeman. The movie is briefly summarized as, "Two terminally ill men escape from a cancer ward and head off on a road trip with a wish list of to-dos before they die." It was engaging and humorous and has since inspired romantic notions among many seniors about taking on adventures, travel, and once-in-a-lifetime conquests before they too "kick the bucket."

Although we reference the term "bucket list" in the title, you won't find here any suggestions like hiking the Great Wall of China, bungee jumping into the Royal Gorge, or swimming with dolphins. But no matter how thrilling or fabulous, they are one and done.

Steve and I are here to make a case for a list of a different sort. A set of readily accessible options for improved well-being.

The choices we offer are of the enduring kind—ones that can change your life forever. These are available for your choosing and then living with intention and are free (and freeing). Most of these are "I choose to be" and "I will…" statements of intention to own your well-being.

> "When you get your, 'Who am I?', question right, all of your, 'What should I do?' questions tend to take care of themselves."
>
> ~ Richard Rohr

Our approach is to offer knowledge about and the living context for each specific, mindful choice we offer. At the beginning of each conversation, we provide a short description of what it will generally cover. At the end of each conversation, we offer a brief statement of intention—a mindful choice for how you *could be* in the world. Throughout our conversations, we explain methods and tools for turning your intention into a continuously renewed commitment. Living your commitment will result in a change in your behavior over time—a new, habitual way of being.

Our version of this list of intentions is within reach for anyone transiting the bucket list years—the last third or quarter of your lifespan—though it is open to people of all ages who wish to live with a greater sense of well-being.

Steve

I confess that until now, I never understood the true meaning of the term "bucket list." Here I was—excited about writing a book with you about bucket lists—without even knowing where the phrase comes from. I learned that the term is derived from the phrase "kick the bucket," meaning to *die*. And that term comes from the 1800s. A man stood on a bucket to put a noose around his neck before kicking it away to allow the rope to stretch out with his feet dangling.

Louis Armstrong put out a jazz song in 1935 called "Old Man Mose" about an old guy who had "kicked the bucket." His pals knocked on his door and couldn't get any response. I listened to it just now and was amused and delighted by how upbeat and joyful the song was. But that's Louie and the joy he brought to everything he sang and played (even, and perhaps especially, in his so-called old age when he continued to play almost every night in towns and wide spots in the road, all over the country.)

Louie's love of life seemed to *increase* the older he got, and loving life is what we're talking about here.

Will

As I passed through my young adult and mid-life years, I secretly held to a belief that the external path I was on (and my acceptance of the indoctrination and conformity needed to make my way out and up) was not a natural state. Somewhere in "there," there was an ember of individuality.

In my senior years of living, I choose who I will be, how I will take care of myself, and engage in my life with greater meaning, purpose, individuality, and authenticity.

Our exploration of mindful well-being choices encompasses the physical, mental/psychological, and spiritual—body, mind, and spirit. We believe that wholeness is discovered when we consciously work with all three together to build a meaningful life.

The well-being bucket list represented by our conversations includes choices about how you see yourself, behave, interpret, react, and participate in the world during your years as an older adult. We offer choices you can embrace as intentions for changing your life from one of deficiency, unhappiness, and pain to one of sufficiency, joy, and wellness.

Steve

It will quickly become evident to our readers that there is a bit of a difference in your voice and approach, and mine. My thinking is often full of blue-sky positivity. My thoughts fly around constantly, intending to capture the elusive butterflies of possibilities. Aging? What's possible? Let's go! Let's fly!

And that can be fun—even valuable—for readers subconsciously burdened by their self-woven webs of limiting beliefs and superstitions, especially about "growing old."

But, on the other hand, I'm sometimes not *grounded*. I'm often naïve. You, your books, and your writing, are grounded. You have two feet planted firmly on the ground. Your research into the facts (which you do so well) is vital to having what we create here be helpful and doable by starting with *knowledge*.

To dig deep, especially to see if you can unearth the old and bleak superstitions and myths around aging, one must have their feet on the ground. That's where the digging happens!

As the rock group Foghat (and many others) sang in *Take Me to the River,* "Take me to the river / Wash me down / Please my soul / Put my feet on the ground." And you do that, Will.

Will

Foghat, Steve, really?!?? One of the things I appreciate about you is your love for music and singing and your wide range of interests. You already got Louis Armstrong and Foghat into this conversation, and we just got started!

And methinks thou dost protest too much about being attached to a balloon with your feet off the ground! Your humor, anecdotes, and optimism fuel our readers and counter what may seem like TMI (too much information) coming from me.

Steve

I am sure that between us, we can strike a balance worthy of our readers. Making mindful choices is about finding and harnessing one's power for creating a life of freedom, joy, and love. It's about developing your humanity to the level of the opportunity you had when you were born into this world. It's about using your last 10, 20, or 30 years in service to yourself and others, with an attitude of gratitude for the opportunity.

You don't have to give up your bucket list of things to do and places to go. For some, that has its place in a fulfilling life. And, you can have two lists! Consider our offering of 29 mindful choices as your *other* bucket list: choices for being better, freer, and happier—at the same time! And may you benefit from our missteps, mistakes, and recoveries!

Steve Chandler, Birmingham, Michigan
William Keiper, Portland, Oregon

Conversation One
A Bucketful of Choices

We introduce the principal human operating system choice, discuss the distinction between doing and being, and explore limiting beliefs.

Will

We have often spoken about the single choice that influences every other decision we make in life. The Mother of All Choices. "Do you choose to be the *owner* of your life and circumstances, or do you accept being a *victim* of everything so that you can stay stuck?"

The owner-victim distinction is eye-opening and inspiring in bringing clarity—in just two words—to our living incarnations. Steve, you've taught thousands of people and have written numerous books on how to differentiate our attitudes and actions in ways that serve our best interests.

The real jewel in this distinction is that we are NEVER stuck where we are. We can learn our way through or out of anything. We have neural pathways in our brains that can support the adoption of new ways of being—no matter our ages. We have unlimited capacity for curiosity, learning, knowledge, and wisdom, throughout our lifespans. We possess the mental flexibility to move past "what we know" or—more accurately—"what we think we know."

This option for transformation *seems* more accessible in our youth. We still feel the lift of the air beneath our wings and see life as a unidirectional upward spiral. Even setbacks are exciting and can be accepted and shrugged off with a simple, "Whatever…." When we ask questions, learn more, and experience new things, life is stimulating and energizing.

Over time, we tend to discover and gradually slide into a state of limitation—knowing what we know. Eventually, we may not even try to challenge our long-trusted "knowledge." Instead, we may decide to live in our self-constructed comfort zones—even if we cannot recall when and under what circumstances we chose to build it in the first place.

Steve

As you mentioned, Will, the choice that lies beneath and drives all others— "Where you will start the process?"—is everything. It is the predictor of our happiness in our senior years. It all starts with this: "Will you be an owner, or choose to be (or stay) a victim?"

Carl Jung said, "We are not what happened to us; we are what we wish to become." Worrying and obsessing over "What should I do?" leads to a life of just coping with every situation as it comes up unannounced, with no reliance on our inner compass (which could have been misplaced).

Will you choose to own your decisions or be a victim of those made for you by others? Will you find ways to remain autonomous or become ever more dependent?

We can't tell you what choices to make, but our suggestions come from our belief that *being* is an infinitely more powerful starting place. When the *being* is clear and strong, the *doing* flows more gracefully and effectively. They go together, and you can feel it.

Will

Each of our lives is rich with many "doing" choices. Every minute of every day, we process the details of where to go, what to do, who to see, what to say, and on and on. We spend our lives evaluating, prioritizing, and making these choices. And we then live with the consequences, or choose to revise, correct, or abandon them by making fresh choices when we have better information.

You and I may have bucket lists with few choices in common. Yet, by adding to and subtracting from them, we make the most of our living years. The only judge of the value of those choices is us; the list can change as we want or need, and we don't even have to write it down. (In my case, writing things down assures I only need to remember where I put the list—not what's on it.)

We sometimes disagree on characterizing the pain of limiting beliefs and the methods for leaving them behind. Still, we've both seen that the science of "what is possible" is irrefutable—we will explain.

Steve

I agree with you about the "pain" you link to living under the weight of unnecessary limiting beliefs. However, almost without realizing it, we often attribute this discomfort to external circumstances and other people instead of the thought itself.

I wrote about these kinds of limiting beliefs in my book, *Reinventing Yourself.*[1] I never felt it would sell because it was such a personal account. Who cares about a guy with a history of bankruptcy, divorce, and alcoholism who reinvented himself? But much to my surprise, it became a bestseller.

My only explanation for that is that readers must have become inspired by concluding, "If that level of a loser can reinvent himself, maybe I can, too."

When I read your recent book, *Untethered Aging*, I saw for the first time that the thrill of personal reinvention could not only continue in these advancing senior years of mine but that there was practical, life-enhancing value in making that happen.

Mindful Choice #1

I intend to actively make opportunistic, directional adjustments in becoming the person I want to be, starting now.

[The choice we present at the end of each conversation is a suggestion for your adoption. If something else comes up for you from reading our conversation, please cross our suggestion out and adopt something that works for you. This is an opportunity for creation and ownership in creating your best life—a powerful new kind of personal bucket list.]

Conversation Two
How to Measure Life Expectancy

We discuss the value of knowing the likely outer limit of our lifespans, raising our awareness of our daily choices, appreciating that living happens today, and that our life's time is not bankable.

Will

Most people do not consult actuarial tables to estimate their remaining years of living. A Google search will quickly return an easy form for you to fill out to get a response to the inquiry, "All things being equal, what age might I live to?"—but I suspect you will not find it anywhere near the top of the list of most popular search inquiries.

In my first book, *Life Expectancy—It's Never Too Late to Change Your Game*[2] (the process through which you skillfully guided me, thankfully), I explored this issue. I believed then and still believe that knowing the likely outer limit of your lifespan can motivate *really* using your time. My own probable "use by" date has been in my thoughts since I wrote *Life Expectancy*. It has become second nature for me to consider it almost every day. I have learned so much about lifespan that if people ask me to estimate their remaining lifespan, I can come close to what a Google inquiry will estimate. I've had (quickly) passing thoughts about replacing the "Guess Your Weight" attraction at local carnivals, but I don't think "Predict Your Expiration Date" would be as popular.

We were all born with the certainty that our last day will arrive sooner or later. Of course, most of us would rather have it come later, But, 13 to 20 percent of those born on the same day in the same year passed away before 65. Although American life expectancies have gotten longer over a single generation—that of the Boomers—the added years have brought many complexities.

We have lived through problems and challenges—seemingly endless waves of them. So, it has been easy to say we will *really* begin to live when the current disruption (whatever it is) is brought under control or resolved through the old reliable healer: the passage of time. Time was on our side--we assumed—and life's end was somewhere well over the horizon.

As we passed through mid-life, it began to register that living is not what happens when "things settle down." Living is *all* the minutes, hours, and days we experience. The challenging ones are just as much "living" as are the moments of joy, celebration, and contentment.

Most of us would agree that experiencing more juicy moments would be a better use of our lives than *waiting* for more of them to arrive. Yet, we spend much of them biding our time for those richer moments to show up rather than creating the conditions that, or becoming the person who, will make them happen.

"Use it or lose it" might seem an easy choice to make. Who would knowingly choose to allow their life expectancy to tick by without trying to stack up moments of happiness and limit the ones that bring us down? But losing something is often the consequence of ignorance and inaction. You may not see these as choices, but passivity *is* an action. Not deciding is—without question—a decision.

Sitting on your hands rather than going for a walk may not seem like a choice to use your life or lose it. But the choices in your remaining years will often be ones of taking action or accepting (or not recognizing) inertia.

When we begin feeling the weight of these passive losses through not deciding, we often wonder, "Where does the time go?" So, let's look at how an average (nonworking) senior spends their days compared with other adults. Most survey results on this subject come to pretty much the same conclusions:

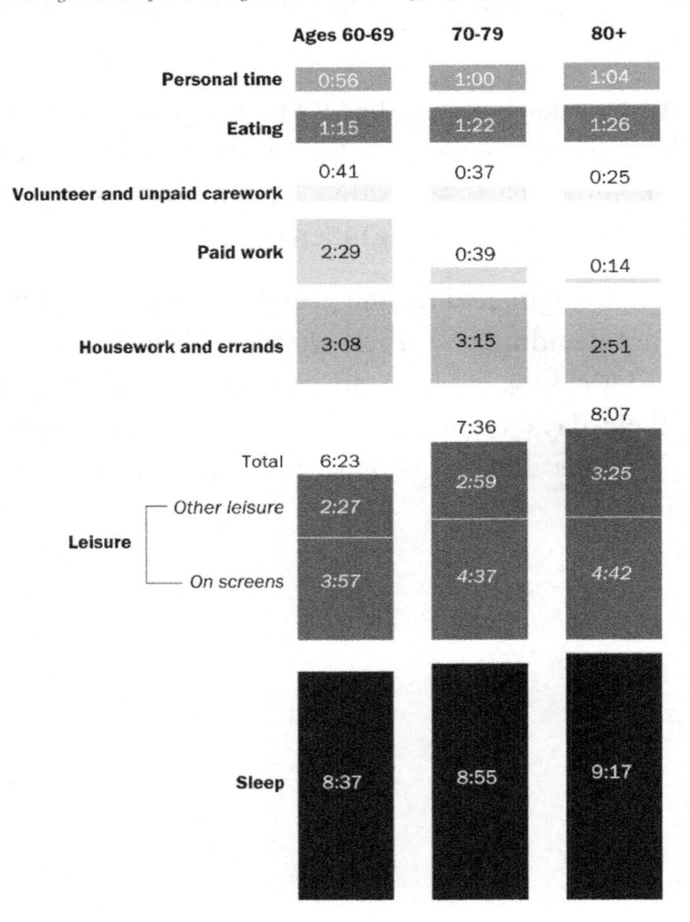

Here is a summary (excluding sleeping):

- Screen time of about four hours is an hour and a half longer than the average adult.

- Household management and errands take about three hours. This includes things like cleaning, laundry, tending to plants and gardens, and other housework, as well as food preparation. It also includes shopping for groceries, other essentials, and other items.
- "Other leisure" time is an additional two-and-a-half hours. Seniors between 65 and 74 spend about half an hour a day reading, and those 75 and older typically spend an hour a day. Socializing is a part of this time, too.
- Eating for about an hour and twenty minutes is 15 minutes longer than an average adult.
- Personal time (relaxing and reflecting) takes up about an hour a day, about twice as long as most working adults spend.
- At 30 to 40 minutes per day, volunteering and unpaid caregiving represent slightly more time than the average adult spends on this type of activity.

Three other interesting points:

- Exercising didn't make this list, but most surveys confirm that 15 to 20 minutes a day would be a high average. More available time doesn't translate into more significant physical activity for seniors. Much more later about this choice and its consequences.
- According to the Bureau for Labor Statistics, an older person with no spouse or other companion in their home spends an average of ten hours of the waking day alone. There are many implications of this isolation and

potentially associated loneliness. Again, we will get into the details of this in a later conversation.

- Working seniors between 65 and 75 average about one hour per day dedicated to it.[3]

We intend to stimulate your interest in alternatives and enhancements to some of these daily activities. We will help you answer the question, "What are some ways I can enliven my living experience each day?"

As in the movie *The Bucket List*, being conscious of potential choices can lead to purposeful decisions for enriching your life while you can.

Steve

The primary areas of focus for me and the clients I coach every day (young and old) are simple: addressing mind, body, and spirit.

To build on your words, Will, I might ask before my day begins, "Where can I create more active choices with greater passion on these three pathways to happiness and fulfillment?"

That question wasn't active for me in my earlier years. It wouldn't have worked for me then because I always thought "passion" had to pre-exist. I thought I'd have *to already know* what specific thing I felt "passionate about" before I could think of bringing *even more* energy to it. And in my days of worry, fear, and discouragement—in other words, most of my days—I had a tough time finding any existing passion.

It took a long time before I learned that I could bring passion to anything I chose. The more time and energy I give to anything, the more passion comes alive. It never had to pre-exist—I could stimulate it any time I wanted.

This revelation was life-changing. And it's a shift available to anybody and everybody, at every age.

If the committed-to category was BODY, I didn't have to be a fitness freak to devote time and energy to move my body. I didn't have to *be inspired* ahead of exercising to start doing it. And the more time I blocked out to do it, the more passion I could give it, especially once I got going.

An outdoor walk sometimes felt tedious and challenging at the beginning. But once I was out and moving, my pace would quicken, and I would get more enjoyment from just breathing and moving.

My commitment to MIND worked the same way. That large, brilliant, and challenging book on my desk would remain unopened for weeks—and then months—if I hadn't been willing to spend some time with it each day and dive into a few pages.

When I moved to Michigan from Arizona, I was in my 70s, older than my parents when they died. So, I considered myself semi-retired, winding down in my career, and looking forward to giving my brain (and the rest of me) a rest.

When I made the first visit to my new doctor, I thanked him for taking me on for "…these final years of my life!" His eyebrows went up when I said "final," and he asked if he could tell me a story.

He told me he'd recently made a house call on a patient of his, a woman who was 102. He said she was physically healthy, her mind was bright, and she was as witty as ever. He had always wondered about her longevity secret until the day he went into her house.

Then he saw it.

"What was it?" I asked.

"Books," he said. "They were everywhere. In bookcases on all the walls. Some were open by her bed, by a chair, on the coffee table, everywhere." She told him she loved reading and was always reading. And that was when he understood: All that reading was keeping her brain active. It had a life-giving effect, in his opinion, on her whole system.

It also confirmed his belief that reading is the ultimate rejuvenator for the brain. A sedentary life leading to ill health and shortened lives doesn't just come from watching a TV screen all day. The lack of challenge to the brain is more depleting than anything else.

And despite all the fashionable recommendations made to older people to play games or work crossword puzzles to keep their brains at a high functioning level, those activities are nothing compared with reading. While reading, one must "remember" the meanings of thousands of words, sentence structures, make sense of new ideas, and follow narratives and story lines.

I went home that day and thought about my reading. And I realized I had already experienced what you pointed out, Will. I was "losing it because I wasn't using it." The less time I spent reading, the harder it was, over time, for me to get into a book. So, I immediately set more time aside for reading. It wasn't long at all before my reading comprehension began to come back, and my old passion for it—the passion I thought I'd lost somewhere along the way—came back as well.

All of this is anecdotal, of course, from a scientific viewpoint. Even my medical doctor's observation was just one case. But that doesn't diminish it for me because it has become experiential and authentic. So, I'd like to take your saying, "Use it or lose it," which is hard-won folk wisdom (as well as being memorable because it rhymes while scaring me) and turn it into the more uplifting "Use it and keep it growing."

As for SPIRIT, I want to get to that later. There's so much there. For now, I'll just quote Albert Schweitzer, who said, "In everyone's life, at some time, our inner fire goes out. It is then burst into flame by an encounter with another human being. We should all be thankful for those people who rekindle the inner spirit."

That encounter with another human being doesn't have to be accidental.

Mindful Choice #2

I choose to raise my awareness of the passage of time and how I am spending it. I will live each day fully and with passion for something or someone that makes my time count.

Conversation Three
Exploding the Mythology of Aging

We discuss some of the central myths of aging and reframing them. We explore optimism and "learned helplessness," and offer more insight into the owner/victim choice.

Will

Aging is the process of moving through passages of time during our lifespan. We are always aging—as babies, children, young and middle-aged adults, and as seniors. Yet, the label "aging" seems to attach only when we have moved into the category of seniors.

Although "aging senior" could describe 50+ million Americans over 65, it has almost become a pejorative term! Let's accept for the moment that making it into the last third or quarter of our life expectancy is a liability in and of itself. We've all heard some of the comments:

"Sarah sometimes forgets things . . ."

"Anthony used to be so thin. But he has gained a lot of weight…"

"LaToya had to quit going for long hikes; it was making her short of breath..."

"Mike's blood pressure got so high they had to put him on medication…"

"Kristy let her hair go gray! She looks so old now…"

"The Sotos had to downsize and moved into a condo…"

If you look again at each of the statements, you will see that they could apply to *an adult of any age*. Now, add this ending to each of them: "Getting old is so hard to watch. It's just sad to see." We have reinforced the mythology of aging as an *unfortunate, sad condition* just by adding the ending.

Also, notice that the words: "Getting old is so hard to watch. It's just sad to see," are about the speaker, not the person or people observed. It is the watcher buying into the concept of decline due to aging. They are helping continue the mythology, out of habit, societal convention, or so they can—without thinking—step into it when their time comes. "Poor me. I've continued living. I'm older than I was yesterday, and last year, and ten years ago."

We will repeatedly make the point that circumstances needn't define us. We have the power of choice and own the decision of how we will act in each situation. It is decision-making with our eyes wide open, and our brain and senses engaged. Life is not happening to you; you are acting on choices.

Steve

If there's a common thread or theme to my past 30 years of professional life, it's that people can change. You and I sometimes use the word "transform" to acknowledge the process and the outcome.

All my books, speeches, seminars, schools, coaching, and leadership training have been about that one thing: the surprising and dramatic changeability of the human being.

This changeability runs contrary to what the world seems to think. Contrary, especially, to what some, perhaps many, older people seem to believe.

I was able to do all this coaching, writing, and teaching work with focus and passion because I was blessed with *certainty*. I was as certain that people can change as I was that people could swim. I had learned both things myself.

Much of my work has been driven by what I have learned through my own experience. I am my own best-case history, and the anecdotes derived from it have become the content of my work. But the main thing about personal experiences is that they *are* anecdotal. They aren't science.

So, when I found the work of Dr. Martin E. P. Seligman, I was thrilled. His studies were thorough, well-presented, and scientifically-based. After that, I began all my seminars by talking about him and what he had discovered. And even the grumpiest and most skeptical people in the room started to get interested.

Seligman's earliest studies were about a psychological phenomenon in animals and people that he called "learned helplessness." The dogs in his studies would try to do things, and after two or three tries, stop trying. Even after obstacles were removed, they still weren't interested. The animals had quickly given in to a sense of inevitability and helplessness in the face of the task, so they quit trying.

His studies of people led to the same conclusions. Enough failures early in life—even perceived ones—and a person would internalize the helplessness they felt and make it a part of their permanent way of approaching life. The resulting worldview and thinking processes were colored by pessimism. The normal starting point for these people is, "I can't."

These studies of learned helplessness made sense, but they were also rather gloomy. But that only lasted for Seligman until one day, he experienced a flash of curiosity. He asked himself, "If we learn helplessness, why can't optimism be learned?"

That's when his studies began in earnest and were eventually chronicled in his classic book, *Learned Optimism,* which I bought and devoured in 1991, the year it came out.

The research was exciting. He and his team studied the lives and mindsets of over 500,000 people. He found that optimism makes you a happier, more efficient, and effective person in life. It increases the likelihood that you will reach the goals you set. And this was the mind-blower:

Optimism can be learned.

Optimism and pessimism are two distinctly different systems of thought. Whichever of the two you are using, you learned it. If you knew the one that leads to low moods, discouragement, and a seeming inability to create a better life for yourself, you might consider learning the other one.

It's never too late. That's our whole message here. Optimism can be learned just like a new language, a musical instrument, or a new app.

Optimism is based on open-minded possibility thinking, learning to experiment, and appreciating what brain scientists have discovered: The brain can change its shape, size, and internal systems at any age. (This is known as neuroplasticity. More details about it in Conversation Twenty.)

Optimism is not to be confused with frivolous and frothy positive thinking, like the cock-eyed optimist in the musical South Pacific: ". . . immature and incurably green." Because genuine optimism is more realistic and effective at solving problems and creating desired outcomes in life, than pessimism.

For example, let's say I'm an older person who hasn't exercised regularly in years. To appease a family member, for a few days in a row I walk around the block. I quickly find that my knee is painful from walking.

If my habit is pessimism, I will say, "This will never work. My knee is too weak for this." And then I'll quit the "madness" after barely putting my toe in the water.

It's a common thought for pessimists of all ages: "This won't work." Or "This can't succeed." Of course, the glass is never half-full—it's always closer to empty.

And as you can see, those thoughts can quickly lead to not starting at all or quitting in the face of challenge and possibility.

But a learned optimist might come home from the walks with a painful knee and ask himself, "Okay, my knee isn't feeling great. What can I do about it? There must be something I can do to keep walking."

A few weeks later, you see him back in the neighborhood wearing a knee brace but walking briskly, getting ready for his next physical therapy session to keep strengthening his legs.

A pessimistic senior trying to log on to her computer and learn to use the Internet might fail to get it the first few times, then get frustrated and say, "This will never work for me. This is beyond me at my age."

Whereas someone who chose optimism as her learned method of thinking about things, upon failing to log on and get started, would say, "Okay, this isn't working the way I'm doing it, so who can I ask to help me learn this? It can't be that hard to learn. Not if my sister can do it!"

Notice that the optimistic thoughts in these examples were about curiosity and possibility. They were thoughts that opened their minds to avenues of discovery. The pessimists, on the other hand, used their thinking process to shut themselves down from what was possible.

You can also see that a mind that is always asking, "What's possible?" will be more effective than a mind that is asking, "What's the point of it all?"

"Pessimism leads to weakness
while optimism leads to power."
~ William James

The most important thing to remember about optimism and pessimism is that they are not permanent personality labels, even though the world (and maybe even you) will want to label you that way. You'll be called (and call out yourself as) a "pessimist" or an "optimist" as if it was a permanent condition. But it's a choice.

And if you're in your senior years like me, you'll be even more likely to believe the cultural myths that teach you that being old is being stuck with who you are: "I'm too old to change now."

The truth says the opposite. You can shift your thinking and your approach whenever you choose to do so. And your brain will cooperate!

Will

In listening to your points about learned optimism, I began to question whether the status labels of owner and victim are sufficient. Do they offer a way out, forward, or through—at least without seeing your dynamic presentation? They are passive labels (though "owner" clearly *sounds* better than "victim"). You can almost feel the weight you would have to carry to crawl out of a state of *victim*hood. Where does one even start to move that load?

In your book *Creator*,[4] you made this owner/victim distinction differently by changing the words. "Will you choose to be a *creator* or a *reactor*?" Creating starts from a *solution* perspective. Reacting starts with Dr. Seligman's point of *learned helplessness* and has us continuing to default to whatever we decided *we couldn't do* in prior circumstances. How we arrived at that decision and whether we were at our best at the time, are not questioned.

I find the descriptors creator and reactor more straightforward. They suggest *action*: we have active choices we can make at each decision point (especially those new or confounding). We get many chances each day to try on creator/reactor, learned optimism, helplessness, and owner/victim.

Even if our lives seem routine, we still make thousands of choices each day. Some research suggests that the average American makes 35,000 decisions each day.[5] What to eat, for example, typically requires over 200 decisions a day. Sometimes, some of those decisions will be to drink or eat what we always do. These are still decisions *not to change* our routines.

Steve

Hang on, Will. When you say, "I began to question whether the status labels of owner and victim are sufficient," I might agree with you if you are only talking about the labels themselves. But, of course, like all other labels, they are insufficient without context, meaning, or explanation. (Just as the word "Google" meant nothing at all to anyone until we learned what it was and what it could do.)

Keep in mind that although these two words are nouns, just like optimism and pessimism, they do not represent permanent states. My entire book, *Reinventing Yourself,* was based on the many seminars I've given on how exciting and life-changing it is to discover that you need not stay stuck in your victim thinking.

Victims feel and speak as if they are challenged unfairly by every little change and new circumstance in life, including getting older. They start from a position of resistance. On the contrary, owners take full responsibility for their responses to life's challenges. They start from a position of possibility.

We will repeat this many times, as it is a core principle for making choices that best serve us.

If I'm in a victim mindset (a habitual way of thinking and speaking about what is happening *to* me), I will feel sure that because I'm older, my friends and family do not look forward to talking to me. But, then again, if all I do is complain and whine in world-weary tones about my poor health and diminishing physical and mental capacity, no wonder they might look the other direction when they see me coming!

On the other hand, an owner thinks through the reality of their circumstances and chooses a response that serves their situational interest. An owner doesn't blame others. An owner rises to a challenge and enjoys the exercise of personal power in making purposeful choices.

What we are talking about here are the *foundational beliefs* that you will start from when making choices. The most powerful tool you have is in *noticing* your starting point for making choices. Will you start with optimism or pessimism? An owner's mentality or a victim's entrenchment? Is your decision process biased in favor of seeing problems or solutions? Acting with creativity or simply reacting?

You can and will find challenges in many decisions you will have to make. But simply deciding where you will start the process is very often the predictor of your level of happiness and contentment in your senior years. So, let's all say goodbye and good riddance to learned helplessness and its perpetual motto, "I can't—I'm too old."

Will

I recall you telling me that when you were starting as a writer, you excitedly took the first pages of a book about motivation to someone you respected as a writer and speaker. You showed him what you had written, and he said words to the effect of, "I wouldn't bother. This stuff has already been written about by outstanding writers."

I am sure you carry the pain of that judgmental statement even today. I also have an anecdote about this issue. When I was starting to write outside of my work life, I shared some of what I was doing with my then-significant other. I was hoping for an honest reaction, but some encouragement, too. Here's part of what she said: "Not only is your writing not good, but it also has no value, and I would be ashamed to show it to any of my friends. In fact, please don't bring it up when I'm around." So, like you, I stayed the course (with the book, I mean), and this one is my eighth.

As you quietly but persistently moved forward with the book concept you shared, it became *100 Ways to Motivate Yourself*,[6] a bestselling book still in print that has impacted thousands of people all over the world. With that single choice, you changed your life and were on your way to becoming a celebrated author. If you had a victim mentality, it more predictably could have gone another way. You could have accepted the words of the man whose opinion you valued and sought. The world would not have heard what you have had to say in your 35+ books, countless speeches, leadership seminars, coaching, and video training.

You intuitively knew what we all eventually learn: It's not

our thoughts that are unique—it is the experience, honesty, and point of view of the writer that are unique. This is true for writing and for most of life's endeavors.

Each of us hears certain words that are similar in meaning but which may individually trigger very different responses. A word that lit you up in the past, or changed your view of the world, will resonate very differently from ones that just rolled off your back like rain off a duck.

Words always matter. I just happen to engage a little more readily with "creator" and "reactor" as descriptors than I do with "owner" and "victim." I can see and hear the action in the words creator and reactor. For me, these words represent solid starting points for making choices.

Steve

Owner-victim choices aside, Will, you have caught something vital and good here.

My coach, Steve Hardison, who guided my transformation from a perpetual victim (of circumstances and other people) to an owner (of my innate creativity), knew to work primarily at the level of being so that change could become permanent. The goal was that my former helpless life of "I never know what to do!" would leave my bio-computer forever.

Whenever I brought one of my innumerable life problems into a coaching session—always in my mood of "I can't do this"—he would ask, "Who would you need to be to do this?" He was interested in working on the foundation in me, not just the anxious activities on the surface.

The brilliant use of your word *where*, referring to the all-powerful place we start any decision-making process, was also something I learned from my life coach. As he declared his commitments, he'd begin them with, "Coming from love..." Over time, I began to see for myself that where I was coming from related to who was I was *being*, not what I was *doing*.

If I would get a nasty email or have to engage in an uncomfortable conversation, and as a part of that process I lost my composure or was triggered by the other person and snapped back defensively, I could look back and ask myself where I was coming from. For most of my adult life, I'd look back and challenge only the doing. "What did I say wrong?" "How could I have handled that differently?" But that's a shallow level of analysis. Both are "doing" level questions and, therefore, ineffective for long-term change.

When I began to ask myself *where* I was coming from, I could see that I was not coming from love or compassion for others. In most cases, I was coming from a place of fear.

With my coach's help, I changed that.

Working to deepen and committedly practice this intention has enabled my best and most gratifying change in my now so-called senior years, when the aging myth says, "I'm too old to change who I *am*." The truth is the opposite. Senior years give you more time and opportunity to wake up and change where you are coming from. It is your choice.

Will

Life is an endless series of situational challenges. These are not things to get over so we can start living. They *are* living. Each of them presents a test for us: Will we accept the circumstances and allow them to dictate our lives? Or will we choose to view those circumstances—no matter how seemingly impossible—as opportunities for creating our way through?

> "A pessimist sees the difficulty in every opportunity; an optimist sees the opportunity in every difficulty."
> ~Winston Churchill

The circumstances are the raw materials, not the finished product. "What can I do with what's here?" We always have a choice to use our unique alchemy to create an outcome that, in some way, better serves us and perhaps others.

Steve

The mind is an amazingly creative tool if it doesn't get calcified with myth, superstition, and labeling. Older people especially tend to immediately stamp a challenging circumstance as "difficult" or "overwhelming," or "impossible." Of course, I want to emphasize, Will, that I'm coming, as usual, from a more anecdotal viewpoint than the proofs from your excellent research.

For example, I have a high-school friend now in his 70s who had hip replacement surgery. His doctor and physical therapist assured him that he would be walking again without pain or problems if he did his follow-up exercises religiously. If he did, he'd be almost as "good as new!"

When he was with his therapist, he did the required exercises. But he found them "just too hard to do" when he was at home.

He acknowledged that had he been in his 20s or 30s, he would have done the required exercises with vigor and enthusiasm, drawing on his body's youthful energy and the optimistic, ambitious mindset he had about his life. He would have known, intuitively, that he had a lot of living to do, and walking (and even running and dancing and playing tennis) were a valued part of his future.

But now? Too hard. What's the point? So, he slumped back into his recliner and watched TV, and anywhere he had to walk, he did so slowly and painfully, and eventually with the help of canes and walkers and other people. It felt, to him, age-appropriate to be less than vigorous in his rehabilitation.

He chose not to remove the debilitating labels from his circumstances. What did he think would happen if he used such words and terms as "tragic" or "overwhelming" or "not worth the effort." For him, the label ran the show: "Too hard for me, I'm old!"

The potential for seniors (who typically will have more physical challenges as they get older) is to reprogram our minds and open our hearts to circumstances and realize: We can choose to view the challenges through the lens of being positive! Challenges, large and small, are not an affront to our well-being. Instead, they can be life-giving games to play *if we are willing to see them that way.*

I noticed when I moved from Arizona to Michigan in my

early 70s, I somewhat unconsciously went out into the world less often, especially during the winters. At the beginning, and without realizing it, I started losing my balance. I had to grab handrails when I walked up and down stairs, and one day I slipped and fell in the snow. It hit me when that happened that the younger me might have slipped but not fallen. It was embarrassing. And at first, I was ready to write it off as just a part of aging.

But the more I investigated, the more I realized that balance takes practice. As I could clearly see when watching my grandson learn to walk, we aren't born with it. And the less of it you do, the less of it you'll have. So, my choice was clear. Do I want to accept the challenge that poor balance is offering me? Or do I want to label it—call it an "unfortunate by-product of aging" that I must live with?

I read about studies of elderly Chinese people doing Tai Chi in the park every morning. They don't fall. Broken hips are almost unheard of. So, I found video tutorials online to watch and learn simple Tai Chi exercises to restore at least some of my youthful balance.

It was my choice to see the challenge differently than I had been. Rather than seeing "challenges" as always being negative—even more so when tied to age—I could see them as a game I was invited to play.

When I was young, if someone "challenged" me to a game of basketball, pool, cards, or any game, the so-called "challenge" was just an *invitation to play*. It wasn't some kind of disrespectful, unkind, affront. So why create and hang onto that kind of story in any circumstance?

The choice was mine. The mind is infinitely creative. As

Shakespeare said, "There is nothing good nor bad—but thinking makes it so."

Mindful Choice #3

I choose optimism and ownership as my pragmatic, enabling, and repeatable system of thought for living into my future.

Conversation Four
The Value of Beginner's Mind

We discuss the value of challenging "what we know," how to create openness to new learning, and the creating of the future from the future.

Will

A new mind enters the game of life each time a baby is born. The newborn joins about eight billion other humans that are already operational. From a physical perspective, her mind represents a tabula rasa—a blank slate—perhaps for the only time in her lifespan. For a moment, the mental cupboard was bare.

Almost immediately, we began to fill that space with whatever came our way. In the beginning, we didn't sort, filter, judge, fear, or otherwise block the process of "clean learning." Over the years, we and others fill it up, arrange it, set things aside for later, lose and forget things, throw things out, pile things up that don't belong together, decide which items are regularly needed, which things are unique, which belong to someone else, which should be kept hidden, and so on. We create a filtering system that is enormously helpful, but which can also become messy and work against our best interests.

The accumulation over our lifetimes of "what we know"

becomes a barrier to gaining new knowledge, and to discovering new ways of looking at existing knowledge. Later, sometimes much later, we learn that trying to return to our original "default setting" of a beginner's mind can be of great help in learning new things. We must raise our awareness of "what we know" to move it, at least temporarily, out of the way.

This beginner's mind for adults is an elective, experiential state, ideally free from judgment, bias, and preconceived notions. These factors are some of many that we accumulate through learning, experience, and the associated interpretive feelings. Our feelings cement "what we know" into concrete forms that are challenging for us to break, even if doing so is in our best interest. A new idea, "just doesn't feel right," and we find ways to resist, perhaps unknowingly.

In Zen Buddhism (and some martial arts practices), a "beginner's mind" is known as Shoshin. It is an experiential approach to learning designed to create an accepting state of mind rather than one in which we allow our filters and existing knowledge to lead us to dismiss new perspectives.

In his book, *Zen Mind, Beginner's Mind,*[7] Shunryu Suzuki describes it this way: "If your mind is empty, it is open to everything. In a beginner's mind, there are many possibilities; in the expert's mind, there are few."

Some of the terms used to describe the state of readiness for receiving new inputs include being open, welcoming, devoid of preconceptions and biases, and ready for possibility thinking.

One way I have found to create that small opening to a beginner's mind is by asking, "At this moment, what more is needed?" When I ask this question of myself, nothing comes to mind. I can identify nothing that would make the moment more complete. I find nothing lacking.

Try using the inquiry, "At this moment, what more is needed?" when you are about to receive new learning in any form and where you can feel some resistance to it. Though it may not work for you in the same way that it does for me, I believe you will find more perfection and calm than imperfection and noise in that moment of asking. In addition, it is a way to clear the sense of being overwhelmed, deficient, or in fear—all of which block the openness required to access—at least in part—beginner's mind.

The "one sentence" guidance I offer to readers, business clients, people I coach, and others I encounter along the way is this: "We can do things differently when we can see things differently." Our objective here is to offer approaches for seeing things differently and present choices that, when selected, can open your path to "doing" with new, creative approaches.

Steve

This choice you offer here, Will, is vital. Unfortunately, the older we get, the less likely we are to be aware of it.

If we rely on our history, including parental guidance, we may use an outdated and uninspired memory bank to create our future. Spiritual teacher Byron Katie recommends the opposite. She says, "Go to the *I don't know* mind" for inspiration. Don't stay stuck in that small, constricted mind that contains all the stuff you already think you know. There's no creativity there.

Werner Erhard distinguishes this choice as "Creating the future from the future." Unless we deliberately work from the future instead of the past, we'll create our lives helplessly driven by our past habits, limiting beliefs, and prejudices.

As you know, because you've been such a successful consultant to companies—especially those in desperate need of seeing things differently—management tends to create the future from the past. They take what they did last year and try to up their performance by a small percent. They don't listen to the most successful business leaders like Jack Welch, whose motto was, "Change before you have to."

As we get older, we face the added challenge of sustaining the courage, creativity, and open-mindedness associated with being young. We may choose to passively accept the learned helplessness inside the thinking that tells us, "There's nothing new under the sun" and "It's a little late in the game to be trying something new" and "I ought to know by now what to do, and the new approach is not it." Then there's the denial of, "It's working fine, why tinker with it?" even when it clearly isn't fine.

An awakening, spiritual or otherwise, can happen at any age, and there are many things we can do that will open our minds to fresh and new possibilities. When we choose to do that, we find that a "beginner's mind" gives us a far more creative and inspiring place to start from than the old, worn-out biographical memory trains of thought ever could.

Mindful Choice #4

I accept the challenge to clear away "what I know" and "what I think I know" so that I may be open to new learning and seeing things differently.

Conversation Five
The One and Only You

We discuss the process of selectively shifting out of conforming behavior, accepting the call of the inward journey, and welcoming the exploration of your latent or budding uniqueness.

Will

Many of us find ways to overlook or stifle our uniqueness, let alone see value in it. This subordination of individuality is especially evident when the gravitational pull of daily living is from the outer world. As children and students, we learn from others: parents, teachers, peers, television and social media, and our own direct experiences. We may develop personal interests, but for the most part, it is a time of learning the basics of what others think we need to know.

The years of growing up and primary education are also ones of learning about and accepting boundaries. Many of us were spoon-fed a vanilla education often geared to the lowest common denominator. Our first 18+ years were often the equivalent of a lobotomy for our creativity and differences, with some occasional exceptions. A less extreme characterization of that process is "going along to get along," a form of surrender that we can easily carry with us the rest of our days.

We learned that conformity is the better part of valor.

Outliers were considered "troubled" for the extra time it took to get them back in line with everyone else. The last thing our educators wanted was a student feeling comfortable marching to the beat of a different drum.

Examining or cultivating the individualist part of ourselves had to wait. By the end of our education, we had completed phase one of what might be described as "indoctrination" in different times and cultures.

"If one does not keep pace with his companions,
perhaps it is because they hear a different
drummer. Let them step to the music
they hear, however measured
or far away . . ."
~Henry David Thoreau

Most of us moved from our primary and secondary education into making a living (at least), forging a career (hopefully), finding and associating with a community (belonging to something), perhaps discovering a significant other or companion (being loved), maybe having children (a family and legacy). This period (which usually lasts for decades) doesn't require a deep dive into our inner values and differences; instead, it is more informed by our reactions to the outer world, and it reflects what we see in others on similar paths.

We are "responders" day-in and day-out—to the boss, a spouse, the children, the customers, the bills to be paid, the challenges, blows, recoveries… to everything demanding actions and answers. For the most part, our heads are down, making sure that one foot follows the other. Views of the horizon can wait.

As we move through midlife, we may feel some stirrings of dissatisfaction with what's behind us and some trepidation that the road ahead looks about the same. Job and career may have seen their best moments, children leave the nest, and the family unit begins to shift to a different configuration. Estrangement and divorce are not uncommon.

More importantly, we begin to question long-held beliefs about our servitude to the outer-facing life, our level of self-satisfaction, and whether this is "all there is." Jumbled in with these questions could be the recognition that more than half of our lifetime has passed. Perhaps there is a sense that there are many unanswered, and even unasked, questions. Non-specific dissatisfaction may take root for a while. A look over your shoulder may bring some feelings of regret. (We discuss regret in our Conversation Twenty-Eight, "Regrets? Too Few to Mention.")

We may have reached late midlife with a view that the years ahead are about physical and mental decline, moving to the sidelines, and passively being pushed out of a society defined by a youth-dominated culture. "Where did my life go?"

For the past ten years, the decade of my 60s, as a business consultant, coach, and author, I have explored aging from many different perspectives. I have come to some conclusions that I want to share with you.

The first is that the secret to a happy and satisfying last third of life is looking inward and examining what is there without judgment (or at least being gentle about it). Despite the conformity that has defined much of our lives, ultimately, we must discover, explore, and appreciate our uniqueness and individuality. To do so, we may have to strip away some scar tissue, regrets, echoes of what others have said (and may believe) about us, and our subjective feelings of success or failure.

The second is to consider shedding some aspects of the identity we assumed to cope with the outside world's demands. This identity was a part of our indoctrination, which in most cases continued through our young adult and middle years. In an address to the Harvard Divinity College, Ralph Waldo Emerson said, "Imitators doom themselves to hopeless mediocrity." It may be the time to quietly say to yourself, "Hello, I've wanted to meet you for a long time. Let's sit together and talk." This silent conversation may be your first opportunity to begin breaking out of conformance.

Third, as much as the choice to better understand ourselves is apparent and accessible, the first step may be to push back—to rationalize why that isn't true for "me." Perhaps at some point you've said or thought words to the effect of:

- "I'm not sure I want to look too hard at myself. I might not like what I see."
- "It's too late, and I wouldn't know where to start."
- "I've never thought of myself as someone to challenge who I am being."
- "It seems like a lot of trouble, and I'm not looking for trouble."

Each of these thoughts represents resistance. We can conjure up many reasons to avoid an inquiry into our uniqueness. The desire to explore, and the opposition to it, are parts of the process.

As older adults, we have experience, education, perspective, wisdom, patience, and a well-developed sense of what's "okay" and "not okay" for us. We have more time for reflection and exploration. We have the chance to develop greater personal insight and wisdom.

Letting go of a lifetime identity requires a move outside a long-established and well-defended comfort zone. But we must "let go to grow." And the cost of putting this off rises with age as there is less time for do-overs. Reliance on the old saw, "time cures everything," is exposed for the avoidance it represents in the face of fewer years ahead.

If you cannot seem to start this exploration, consider that we may have arrived at an age where even the "conforming you" isn't seen or valued as much. We conformed, we subordinated our uniqueness and stifled the voice that wanted so often to speak up. And now where are we?

What are the risks? If any at all are seen, I assure you they are greatly overestimated. There are eight billion people in this world, but nobody is going to get in your way if you want to explore being you. Or just put it to a vote. You will win every time: one to eight billion, in your favor. The eight billion don't matter and don't care. Only your vote counts. If you want to "do," you "can do."

We aren't and have never been our conformity. It was and is a mask, a consequence of socialization and cultural system control. Uniqueness and individuality are our essences. Saying hello to myself as a senior was like shedding the weight of a suit of chainmail armor. I feel better than ever before, in the skin I have had as my wrapper since birth. What mattered wasn't outside—somewhere out there in the world around me—it was inside all the time.

I have been able to see, and grow to appreciate, my differences. So many were there from the start but were overlooked while I tended to almost everything else. I discover more of my uniqueness day-by-day in what have become the happiest days of my life. I believe this is due to seeing myself at a level of honesty that is liberating. In societal (and personal) terms, I'm certainly not perfect. But idiosyncrasies and even wackiness can be beautiful too.

Imagine living in alignment as the distinctive—one and only—you. Imagine having mind, body, and spirit working together as intended. Now is the time to make inner discovery a priority. To uncover or be reminded of your unique qualities, ways of looking at the world, creativity, passion, engagement with life—and to choose priorities that feed active happiness. These are some of the building blocks of meaning.

The fact that those around you, including friends and family, may not understand this process of exploration and discovery is of no consequence. If you can be at your most authentic, even-keeled, and happy, is any explanation required? Those who matter will get it, now or eventually.

And who cares if it took us 60, 70, or 80 years to get here? Better now, than later—or never.

Steve

I like how you have distinguished the limiting burden of conformity from the thrill of discovering "me" and living from a position of who I want to become.

Fear of what others think is the foundation for conformity. This fear sets its deepest roots in the teenage years when puberty and adolescence exaggerate the hunger for love and approval. We don't want to seem "weird" or unusual in any way because, especially in those years, any shame or humiliation can be devastating. So we conform.

But as you said, in our later years, there is a huge opportunity to reach back and reconnect with the fearless self-expression we demonstrated as young children. To the time when there was no such mental restraint as the ongoing fear, "What will people think?"

It is unnecessarily tragic when older people unconsciously or even consciously continue surrendering to conformity. It takes on the nature of giving up.

As the years go by, we collapse into what societal myths say is age-appropriate. Feeling and expressing joy in simply being alive is no longer acceptable. Grandfather should sit in a lawn chair softly smiling at the children kicking the ball in the yard—instead of running out and joining them. It doesn't feel age-appropriate for him to dance or sing or play ball or jump for joy. What would people think? "He's finally, really, lost his marbles!"

Several years ago, I met up with some high school friends I hadn't seen since the 1960s. Although claiming to be perfectly healthy, one of the women walked with us on the streets of Boston, hunched over, shuffling her feet, clutching an old-fashioned purse, and wearing a dress that looked like it had once belonged to Martha Washington. She was in her 50s but had already surrendered (prematurely, I thought) to conform to how she thought older people should present themselves.

I finally couldn't stand it any longer and took her aside and said, "What are you doing?"

She said, "I don't know what you mean."

I said, "I mean, we came here to have fun in Boston and be with each other like we did in our high school days, and you look and act like you just stepped out of a glass case in the American History Museum we just left."

She wasn't comfortable with where the conversation was going, and I realized that what I had said was awkward and unwelcome.

Looking back on that day, I can see how trapped she was inside the superstition that we must conform to the "age-appropriate." Instead of reflecting on or challenging them, we are led around by the depressing thoughts you identified, Will:

- "I'm not sure I want to look too hard at myself. I might not like what I see."
- "It's too late, and I wouldn't know where to start."
- "I've never thought of myself as someone to challenge who I am being."
- "It seems like a lot of trouble, and I'm not looking for trouble."

I wince when I read those thoughts spelled out so clearly. I have had those thoughts myself. They usually come and go quickly, so I don't fully realize what they're saying about me. But I can still feel the downward pull when they pass through.

Alice Walker, the author of the Pulitzer Prize-winning novel *The Color Purple*, famously said, "People give up their power by thinking they don't have any." But that's the whole point here. Look clearly, don't look away. See what you're doing to yourself. Do you want that?

It really is a choice.

Mindful Choice #5

I choose fearless expressions of my personal power through discovering and owning my uniqueness and authenticity.

Conversation Six
Your Money or Your Time?

We discuss the income and affordability treadmill, reducing financial anxiety, reframing lifestyle considerations, living within or below your means, and seeing work differently.

Will

With a gun in your face during a robbery it wouldn't take long to decide between parting with your money or giving up your remaining years of living, Unfortunately, for most of our lives, we lack this kind of clarity. Instead, we pursue money and material things and spend big chunks of our days, months, and years doing so.

Just paying taxes on our income takes more working days each year. Covering the rising costs of essentials take even more. We are likely to have more debt at the end of each working year than greater savings, if any.

There is a certain numbness that takes over when it comes to this bargain. It makes sense, of course, that making a living consumes most of the days in many of our living years. Most of us have insufficient wealth to enable the choice of earning money versus spending time doing what we want to do.

When it comes to the choice of money or time, aging is the great equalizer. There is a substantial variance in earning power and living standards among our citizens for most of our lives. However, this divide significantly narrows as we approach and live through our senior years. Individuals who have earned higher incomes during their working years will typically move to lower-income ranges during their senior years. After 65 our resources diminish but also stabilize to a large extent, and our discretionary time grows.

Over 95 million adults aged 55 and over live in the U.S.—54 million are 65 and older. I offer three data points that tell the basic financial story of American seniors, no matter the lifetime of effort:

Eighty percent of fully retired people 65+ had a median annual income of $22,005. For those still earning work income, 50 percent had less than $27,398 in yearly income from all sources.

- Without Social Security benefits, about 40 percent of Americans ages 65+ would have incomes below the poverty line, all else being equal.[8]
- Over 200 million American adults have less than $5,000 in their savings accounts. Over 115,000,000 indicate they have *no savings*.[9]

Like it or not, most nonworking seniors live on lower and fixed incomes, greatly enhanced, in most cases, by Social Security checks. Given the tectonic shifts in the world of work during and following COVID-19, it is more problematic today to supplement income in retirement. Yes, you can do it, but it will require persistence and some luck.

Even if you are fortunate to have greater resources than most, it may not relieve the anxiety associated with the potential of outliving those assets. When asked, "What do you fear most: outliving your money in retirement or death?" Sixty-one percent of survey respondents said they were less fearful of dying. Even more startling was the finding that among the married respondents in their late 40s with dependents, the number afraid of outliving their assets rose to 82 percent.[10]

Ninety-two percent of U.S. adults agree that nothing makes them happier or more confident in life than when their finances are in order.[11] At the same time, most people's definition of success continues to favor relationships, health, and lifestyle over material possessions, career, and wealth.

In a recent survey, the top six attributes of a successful life included:

- "Spending quality time with family."
- "Having a good relationship with your spouse or partner."
- "Being healthy."
- "Having a good work/life balance."
- "Being a good parent."
- "Being financially prepared for the future."

It requires time and attention to release the pervasive presence of financial anxiety. Still, eventually, most seniors find ways to live within their means and make way for a life that is more about the value of time than money. The question then becomes, "How long should you wait before choosing time over money?"

Steve

I'm going to go in a different direction because I don't see this as a good choice. Or at least not an obvious choice.

You imply that the time I spend providing a service that produces income is not, in relative terms, a good trade-off in my life. It's just money, without any other redeeming value. But even worse than that, it suggests a money choice removes *otherwise valuable time* from your life.

I know (or am guessing) you don't mean that Will, so I look forward to you straightening me out on this. But for now, let me continue, based upon William Blake's theory that "… a fool who persists in his folly will become wise."

Let's say an older person who's been lonely and bored in his first years of retirement decides to get a job at a local food market. It changes his world from boredom to happy engagement with people. He sets his alarm earlier than he has to because he loves showing up early for work. The people he works with are like his new family.

The extra money he makes may have no relevance to his financial security because his retirement savings were always more than enough.

Do we say he chose money over time? No.

Or the multi-millionaire quarterback playing way beyond the typical retirement age wins the Super Bowl. When they ask him how long he intends to keep playing, he says, "I'll play as long as I still love the game and can make a positive contribution to this team."

Is he choosing money over time? No.

I concede that my opposition to this as a choice one must make is probably wide of the mark you're trying to hit here.

But I don't want to assume, as so many people in our society do, that anything done for money is a sacrifice of time; that time spent working for an income is robbing us of life.

You hear it everywhere:

> "Poor Dad, he had to go back to work."
>
> "Oh, wow, didn't he save enough?"
>
> "No… well, he thought he had, but then he had to deal with that lawsuit."
>
> "Oh, jeez, so now he had to find a job and work? How tragic. How absolutely unfair, demeaning, and debilitating. What a vicious, heartbreaking twist of fate for Dad."

The problem with that mindset is that it misses an undeniable fact: work can be fun. And you and I get to be in creative control of how much fun we make it, no matter what age we are.

I've set you up here, Will, to make a counterpoint that will encourage the jury to disregard (most of) everything I've just said!

Will

You make a fair point that spending time working is a valid, maybe superior, way to spend much of adulthood and a portion of our senior years. There are many benefits to be gained, including social engagement, satisfaction, escaping boredom, or even wanting to stay on the path that has been our comfort zone for decades.

I failed to make my meaning fully clear: Being a *hostage* to work, rather than choosing it, could make someone feel like they're squandering the precious sand streaming into the bottom of their life's hourglass. (I thought if I dressed it up a bit, you might come around.)

If you *must* work to make ends meet, and many of us do, that is not a choice. What IS a choice is framing it in the terms you mentioned. Not as struggle, pain, or depression, but as a positive engagement with the outside world that yields some needed income.

We needn't listen to or care what others think about the 78-year-old cashier serving them at the carwash. As has always been the case, others can make up whatever stories they want about us. If I work, whether I need to or not, my choice is to make it a positive part of my time on Earth.

In my case, I "work" almost every day at writing. I am hopeful that one day there will be a financial return on my time investment. It hasn't yet happened, and, for now, it needn't. I choose to do it because it stimulates me and satisfies my need to learn more about the world and my place in it. I am electing not to do many things that some would say is a much better use of my time, including more consulting and coaching to produce income.

I *choose* to spend my time in what others might call the torture of doing research and writing all day while chained to a desk. My positive perspective on work reflects that of the lyrics of a Molly Hatchet (the Southern rock band) song, "One Man's Pleasure": "One man's loss is another man's gain / One man's pleasure is another man's pain." Ironically, the lyric was probably derived (and I'd bet unknowingly) from what the Roman poet and author Lucretius wrote in *De Rerum Natura* (The Nature of Things): "What is food to one person may be bitter poison to others." (You referenced Louis Armstrong and Foghat earlier. Although it is not a competition, notice that I got Molly Hatchet and Lucretius into the same paragraph!)

We agree, Steve, that if your needs, financial or otherwise, limit your choices—the time you spend working can yield life-enhancing benefits beyond income. Even when we lack the power to change the circumstances, we still control how we react to them. Nobody can take that choice from us, in work or any other dimension of living.

Mindful Choice #6

I accept my status and relationship to money or will proactively change my lifestyle to eliminate financial anxiety. I will do what is required, using the best of my resourcefulness and creativity.

Conversation Seven
Remembering the Light Within

In this conversation, we unpack the meaning underlying the quotation: "We are not human beings having a spiritual experience. We are spiritual beings having a human experience." ~ Pierre Teilhard de Chardin

Will

You and I see the world of thoughts and things as a type of all-you-can-eat buffet. We sample this philosophy, that part of a religious approach, a piece of an essayist's musings, some song lyrics, a poet's creation, and morsels from the great writings of authors known and ignored. We don't overlook Dr. Seuss or Rainer Maria Rilke. We are unafraid to create word picture mosaics from these bits to educate and inspire our readers.

We believe that the world both "moves in mysterious ways" and is "in alignment" in remarkably consistent ways. Therefore, we seek apparent (and not so obvious) connections from diverse sources to illustrate the options for "being" as older adults, especially from psychological and spiritual perspectives. We highlight those connections to show, wherever you are and whatever you are doing, you are at your best when your thinking and spirituality are seamlessly connected.

One of the things I have known most of my life, but ignored or buried for various reasons and excuses, is the pure power of having my values and actions in alignment. I have confirmed this by looking back at my best thinking, work, creativity, balance and centeredness, humanity, and happiness. My optimal performance and happiness were evident when this alignment was present and accounted for.

My appreciation and understanding of the power in this "alignment" resulted from repeatedly reaping the consequences of being *out* of such a positive flow. When I strived for excellence with integrity, my life has worked well. But when I missed a step or went sidewise or backward, I always felt the pain and consequences of failing to live in alignment.

I couldn't always recognize this friction at a conscious level until after the fact—maybe long after. In the moment, I often lacked the insight to see the importance of intentional alignment of values and actions in ways that might best manifest in each situation.

To take this one step further, Drs. Mary and Ron Hulnick, founders and directors of the University of Santa Monica, wrote about alignment in their excellent book, *Remembering the Light Within*:

> When you hold a clear intention, your thoughts, feelings, and behaviors—including your words—align. As you align your purpose, choices, words, and actions with the outcomes you wish to experience or manifest, you initiate inner alignment with the Essence of who you are—a Divine Being having a human experience!

Although our bodies are the physical transport vessels for

living, most of the awareness I am referencing lies in the mental, psychological, energetic, and spiritual realms. Understanding and developing these aspects of our beings, and discovering the connections among them, can and should become some of the work of our remaining lifetimes.

Today, I am a happy explorer of these realms and a voracious consumer of the teaching and writings of those who have long considered these matters. I had my head down and was deep in the ground-level human experience for much of my adulthood. I have now seen the potential for connecting and aligning that wisdom with a spiritual component. I can't yet fully wrap my head around the part of the de Chardin quote, "We are spiritual beings having a human experience," but I am hopeful.

Steve, you have been exploring these issues for decades now. And you were recognized with an honorary degree from the University of Santa Monica for your insights, teaching, and coaching. Can you offer some guidance here for me and our readers?

Steve

The good news is that the USM systematic approach to Spiritual Psychology opens the door to appreciating what de Chardin said in his short and provocative quote. USM doesn't have a corner on this insight, but it is the one I know best.

What I loved most about my time teaching and consulting at USM was seeing how effectively their programs delivered systems to their students for true psychological and spiritual transformation. Through interactive teaching programs, they demonstrated that when spirituality and advanced psychology are successfully integrated, the change in the student can be rapid, profound, and long-lasting.

My life as an author and coach has focused on this kind of transformation: discovering that we are spiritual beings having a human experience. Can people really change? Or are they stuck inside a permanent personality? And if they *can* change, how does it happen?

There's a clue to how it happens in the title of the latest book written by Drs. Ron and Mary Hulnick, which you referenced, *Remembering the Light Within.* I've recommended it to countless clients, friends, and family members.

The "Light" they talk about is our true nature, divine creativity, and innate well-being. It's who we really are—the good stuff inside—which we will discuss in Conversation Twelve. Its realization can be harmonized with the great spiritual teachings. It is the "kingdom of heaven" within you, the "Buddha nature" permeating one's being before thought, and it is equally there and accessible to religious non-believers who appreciate the science behind the quantum energy field and universal consciousness.

The concept of the "Light" is deceptively simple: It's already within! You've got it and waking up to it will enlighten you to infinite creative possibilities for change.

What excites me about our bucket list of mindful choices here is the challenge of inspiring and "enlightening" us older people to the possibility (and, indeed, doability) of creating ongoing, positive change *against the tide of those who think we can't*. We've all heard it said: "It's too late." "Our habits are too ingrained." "Our willpower has softened." "Our arteries and attitudes have hardened." "Our future has dimmed down to the barely visible."

Despite all the evidence to the contrary, this mythology is almost universally bought into and accepted as truth by many. There are legions of examples all around each of us.

Yet it's not true for you, Will. I watch you at 70, exercising your mind, body, and spirit, creating influential books and essays faster and better, and enjoying life more than ever. And it's not true for me either. I'm thriving in life. I'm expanding my creative writing and loving my work and music and nature and family more than I ever have before. Or consider Ron and Mary Hulnick, also in the "advanced" age group, who deliver their courses at USM with more spirit and impact than ever.

Are we—and all the other "older" people we know (and know of) who are loving the advanced years of life—weird outliers? Or have we found ways and *made choices* to ignore (or put into perspective) the aging stereotypes? To have our senior years be about answering the question Ron and Mary Hulnick ask: "How can we thrive by remembering and being uplifted by the already present Light within each of us?"

Mindful Choice #7

I will actively explore my spiritual frontier, seeking to have my unique aspects in alignment and remembering and embracing the innate well-being and spiritual light that is already mine.

Conversation Eight
Letting Go to Grow

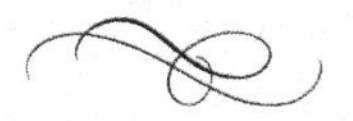

We discuss the need for creating options ahead of change, ongoing assessment of the possibilities for supporting well-being requirements, debunking the myth that aging means "I can't," and the value in creative reinvention.

Will

I led and was part of enterprises from startups to companies listed on the major stock exchanges during my business career. As all businesses grow and mature, management must challenge the beliefs that led them to success.

An existing or new competitor (or worse, a customer) may one day deliver a wake-up call that you've fallen behind. One or more competitive threats may show up in your marketplace in the form of different and better products or an approach to more attractive and cost-effective services. As a result, the threat to the comfortable living that has fed you, your family, your employees, and other stakeholders, may feel like an armed guerilla assault coming while you are in a deep sleep.

One of the hardest things for successful businesses to do is adapt to changes that *gradually* occur. The need for innovation typically doesn't rise to the level of consciousness when the pace of change is slow. Instead, it is overwhelmed by the success of the moment and the reactivity that occurs day by day. Inbound interruptions seem to fill all the hours and take all of the organizational energy.

Then one day, you realize that while you were legitimately busy dealing with your "right now," the world changed. Seemingly suddenly, others have swamped your solutions and processes that may have once been world-beating.

Along my own path, I became fascinated by the term and then the concept of *creative destruction.*[12] In economic terms, creative destruction is the purposeful deconstruction of long-standing practices to make way for innovation.

Today's tech giants have made their versions of creative destruction a formal part of their organizations and cultures. Rather than waiting for a competitor to create something new that could affect the growth and success of their business, they design their companies to do this through their efforts. They *insist* that assumptions and even long-proven ways of doing things be openly and aggressively challenged. Employees and other stakeholders who confront and challenge the status quo are celebrated rather than viewed as troublemakers.

The gap between human adaptability and the rate of technology innovation is akin to the difference between riding a carousel and a rocket. The stewards of creative destruction in the tech giant companies and many other businesses are committed to closing this gap.

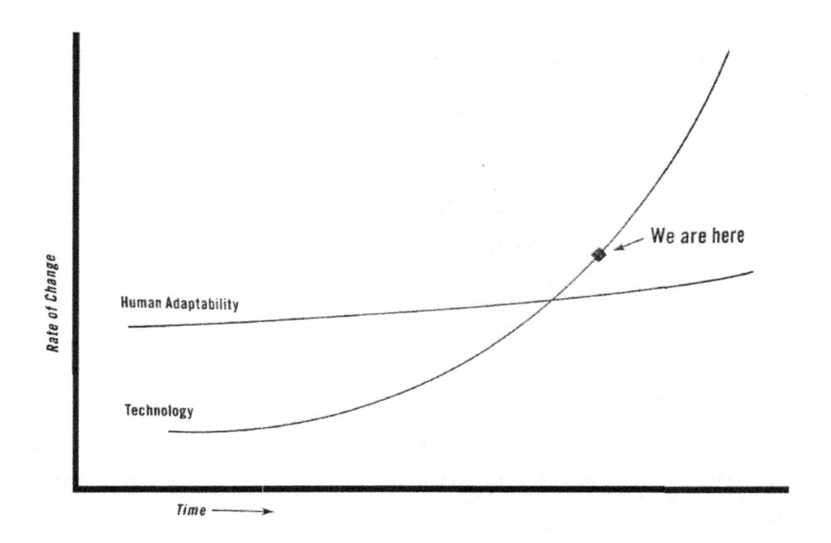

Eighty-eight percent of the firms listed on the Fortune 500 in 1955 are gone. These companies were among the innovators of their day. But they have gone bankrupt, merged, or still exist but have fallen out of the ranking. Just since 2000, 52 percent of the companies in the Fortune 500 have suffered the same fate!

In addition, some once iconic brands are gone or greatly diminished primarily due to a failure to innovate. Examples include Polaroid, Toys “R” Us, Pan Am, Borders, Tower Records, Kodak, and Blockbuster (which at its peak employed 84,300 people worldwide and had 9,094 stores).

Success is measured by looking back, but continuing it requires challenging the status quo. Of course, doing this is as much the case for humans as it is for businesses. However, what is working well and serving your interests today needn’t be thrown out. But it may not be wise to keep pulling the existing (maybe dusty) file folders from your history and moving them into the cabinet that should contain the blueprints for your future. The extreme rate of disruptive change in our world makes this approach naïve and reckless—for companies and humans.

"Life can only be understood backwards but it must be lived forwards."
~ Søren Kierkegaard

As mentioned earlier, one of my favorite phrases to live by is, "You can do things differently when you can see things differently." You could say one year, "I am never moving from this house in this town. They are going to have to take me out of here in a box!"

A year later, you may have lost your job, spent your life savings on health care for yourself or a loved one, and now cannot afford the rent or mortgage payment where you have comfortably lived for years. Moving to a more affordable rural area in another state is an alternative.

Your circumstances have cracked your comfort zone. Now, you see things differently! You might even be on the edge of an adventure that changes your life for the better. You *can* do things differently! (And you can take the "box" with you.)

Despite what we tell ourselves, moving to a more affordable or appropriate location is just one example of something that's never beyond consideration. As seniors, Steve moved from Arizona to Michigan within the past few years, and I moved from New York to Oregon. Did the moving disrupt our routines for a while? Absolutely. Were we entirely sure we could make it happen? No, but we overcame our doubts through our willingness to see our living circumstances differently. Was the new locale different than where we were before? Yes. And we are both thriving in our new environments.

In all matters, permit yourself to consider alternatives, even ones that seem outrageous. There may be a seed in that creative process that could lead to a new option. Think of it as a game to play: the “What If” game. What if you could teach yourself to regularly make these kinds of assessments of your comfort zone and challenge the things that have become your usual way of going through life?

One way to do this, Steve, is to use the process you learned from your then-psychologist, Nathaniel Branden. As I recall, Dr. Branden asked you to create sentence stems and then complete them with six alternative endings to create some options for yourself.

Some basic ones (that can apply in many situations) are, “Is it true that....?” Or “Could I shift my....?” Or “I have always wanted to....” Completing these stems could provide insight into what is working or not, and some potential creative solutions to select and implement. This approach is one method of exploring “possibility thinking.” A decision to act, and when to do so, can be saved for another day, if you choose.

For our personal lives, it may be that “destruction” of our existing comfort zones is too strong a word. But exploring and becoming open to creating a new way of being—even in incremental steps—can lead to greater possibilities for living. I am sure you will have more to say about this, Steve.

The questions above (and many others that could be created) can be explored with friends, family, and even trusted advisors. The conversations could assist in reframing the current situation and enable seeing things differently—including simply noticing the *multiple* options available in most cases.

Once we can raise our level of "noticing" the potential options, we will discover an unending stream of choices to purposefully create our path forward. Hopefully, our conversations here will provide grist for the mill of "creative reinvention."

Steve

You have cleverly referenced two myths here. It is essential to debunk, dispel, and eliminate them both!

The first is that creativity is only about adding and producing new stuff. Accepting this eliminates the world of creations that result from taking away and minimizing. For example, this was the case with Michelangelo's statues. He took marble slabs that he turned into beautiful sculptures, including the world's most famous, the *David*. He had a vision of David when he saw the marble slab and then used his hammer and chisel to *carve away* (and creatively destroy) what wasn't needed to realize his vision. Sometimes this is characterized as "releasing the beauty already there."

On a more mundane and practical level, it is akin to "creating" a more beautiful garden by *removing* the weeds and brush, or "creating" a more beautiful home or office by *eliminating* the clutter and mess. When I write books, I notice I can make them tighter and more impactful by *removing* redundant and unnecessary sentences, paragraphs, and sometimes whole chapters in the editing process.

All these creations involve pruning and removing things to end up with something more functional, appealing, or better able to grow and thrive. It's a vital part of the creative process, and it often takes more courage than just adding things.

The second myth you've exposed here is the one that says that once we reach a certain advanced age, we are stuck with what we've got and where we are in life. You mentioned our recent geographical moves as an apt metaphor.

Kathy and I were living in Arizona and had traveled a couple of times to attend my high school reunions in Michigan. Each time we were there, she talked about how beautiful the neighborhoods were, and comments on the green landscapes, the water, and the incredible classic architecture. We didn't have these elements in Arizona, at least not in the same way. She'd say, "I *would have* loved to have lived here!" As if that option had passed us by because of the widely accepted and unquestioned myth that aging means you're stuck where you are (and in every other way)!

These thoughts came up for both of us frequently enough that we began to question *why* we thought we were stuck. We couldn't find any valid reason, so we found new mindsets: "Why not?" and later, "Let's just do it"! We embraced the move, and while we often return to visit our family and friends who are still in Arizona, we love living in Michigan with the beautiful and dramatic seasonal changes and the old-fashioned Midwestern friendliness and support of our neighbors.

It was a great affirmation that we can and must be willing to challenge the myth that aging is synonymous with limitation. We were buying into the brainwashing that says, "You no longer have the freedom to do what you want—after all, you're seniors!" We needed to listen to and challenge the language of resistance (such as Kathy's, "I *would have* loved to have lived here"). And even the exploration can be stimulating and fun.

"What IF?" We possess more freedom as seniors if we will wake up and challenge the old mythology.

Mindful Choice #8

I will actively consider creative options for practical and adventuresome changes that can ease my way, enhance, or simplify my life. I will challenge "I can't because..." thoughts.

Conversation Nine
Create the Family You Want to Have

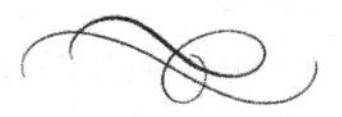

We explore the wisdom and implications for seniors revealed in this quotation from Richard Bach: "The bond that links your true family is not one of blood but of respect and joy in each other's life. Rarely do members of one family grow up under the same roof."

Will

We can all find relationship dysfunction in our growing-up and adult years. For some, this can start with nuclear families. Maybe this is because we had no choice in the matter—the DNA lottery being what it is. We had no choice but to play the hand we were dealt at birth. Conversations with our peers prove that dysfunction seems to have run amok in almost every family—in different ways. One person's anguish could be another's ideal.

When we were children, our circumstances (whatever they were) represented our "normal." We may have dragged that version of "normal" along with us through the years. Or, if we were lucky, someone along the way showed us an approach to family navigation and nurturing that was more in alignment with how we wanted to live. Or, if we were even luckier, we observed the best of family relationships around us and chose to emulate the good parts to create our own "better" version.

I always thought that my story was unusual. My father left our home (and his four children) when his oldest child (me) was six. By the time I was nine, my mother had concluded it would be best to send me off to live with some relatives I had never met. It turned out to be the best thing that could've happened to me, and perhaps she knew it.

The first step of this journey took me from Farm Country, Illinois, to San Diego, California. This relocation immediately opened vistas of a bigger world of opportunity in education, work, travel, and family potential. I didn't see and couldn't have seen those from the perspective into which I was born. In any event, I didn't return "home."

My story caused me to think differently about family throughout my life. I later made mistakes trying to match myself with significant others *and* their families at the same time. Both were equally important to me. Of course, it is hard enough to make a sound choice in *either* case but finding some equilibrium in both was impossible. As a result, I left a trail of poor decisions, sadness, and relationship breakage in my wake.

I came to know family estrangement at an early age—and it is a common condition. David Brooks writes, "At least 27 percent of Americans are estranged from a member of their own family, and research suggests about 40 percent of Americans have experienced [family] estrangement at some point… [Joshua] Coleman, the author of "Rules of Estrangement," argues that a more individualistic culture has meant that the function of family has changed. Once it was seen as a bond of mutual duty and obligation, and now it is often seen as a launchpad for personal fulfillment. There's more permission to cut off people who seem toxic in your life."[13]

I think of family differently today. I see it as something to be assembled to fill in the parts of life where there are gaps. As seniors, it is almost impossible to cover all our wellness requirements individually. Whether it is for basic necessities, companionship, transportation, navigating the health care system, keeping mentally sharp or something else—we all need assistance from time to time.

Furthermore, what is needed will likely change along the way. Your physical or mental health could shift. Your assets and resources could diminish. Your support network of friends and acquaintances could ebb away. It is wise, not calculating or fakery, to reach out to people you think can help whenever those needs arise. However, there is a "but."

BUT you must bring something to the relationship, too. No matter your circumstances, you have something to offer. It doesn't have to be tangible. It could be spiritual support, listening, encouragement, advice based on your experience (parenting, work, budgeting), or something else. "Family" becomes a mix and match of needs and resources. Giving and receiving is a bargain that works for all parties to this "family."

"What do we live for, if not to make life
less difficult for each other?"
~George Eliot

In many cultures, there are long traditions of the younger

generations caring for the elders. This care could include living under the same roof and eating at the same table for many years. However, even in cultures where this commitment for support was once deeply respected, such as Japan, it is much more unusual today. One of the main reasons is simply the cost of housing and feeding another person.

Unfortunately, in a culture dominated by "youthfulness," the elders often become invisible, or afterthoughts. Older Americans' routine social dismissal and rejection (implicit or explicit) diminishes their value. This social diminishment contributes to the epidemics of seniors' loneliness, chronic health conditions, and health management through a default to medication solutions, among many others. More conversation about each of these factors is upcoming.

Given our ability to connect in new ways at every living stage, a new kind of virtual family is possible. Your original family members can be a part of this structure if they are willing (and you can accept the strings and conditions that may come with them). If one or more of your existing family members has become an unwelcome burden on your ability to take care of yourself, it may be in your best (or only) interest to find an uplifting path through the development of a new or expanded family.

To repeat the Richard Bach quote with which we started this conversation: "The bond that links your true family is not one of blood but of *respect and joy in each other's life*. Rarely do members of one family grow up under the same roof." [Emphasis added.]

The family you create can include people who have been lifelong friends (whether near or far) and fellow church, club, or community members. Acquaintances of people you already know can be part of it. People who have knowledge, expertise, or resources that you do not have, but require, can be a part of it. The point is to cover all the needs you may have for living and staying in a state of wellness. I must reiterate that this is a two-way street and goes beyond material needs. You must be "in" for contributing, or it won't work. Think of it as a state of living with a spirit of mutual generosity.

I see this virtual family as a new form of the American family. Seniors collaborating with other seniors. Seniors collaborating with those of any age who care about them, whether family members or not.

I am cringing a bit, Steve, as I realize my points could sound like I am trashing the willingness of the "traditional American family" to care for and about their elders. *I'm just saying*: not every senior has a built-in, willing-and-able family to check-in on them, let alone care for them in a time of need. Therefore, in the interest of self-reliance, there must be a way through. "Build-a-Family" is an option. Richard Bach said it much better.

I expect you will set me straight, and I'm ready for it.

Steve

I'm not uncomfortable with your premise here. It may surprise you to hear, but I think you're right on target.

Coincidentally (or not), in my reading about exercise and its positive effects on the brain, I've also run across studies showing that social connections and interactions with others positively impact brain and heart health, especially in older adults.

The health care website MercyCare.org reports that socialization will lead to "better mental health—it can lighten your mood and make you feel happier and lower your risk of dementia. Social interaction is good for your brain health and promotes a sense of safety, belonging, and security. It allows you to confide in others and let them confide in you."

Of course, for most of us getting into the senior years, we have often lost our groups, connections, friendships, and as you point out so clearly, we may no longer have a traditional "family" with which to interact.

This brought to mind the old song, "I Ain't Got Nobody… and Nobody Cares for Me." It's a blues tune written in 1915 that has been recorded by many artists over time, including Louis Prima, Leon Redbone, and even Mos Def. And who can forget the hilarious scene in *Young Frankenstein* when Igor bursts out singing it?

Although "I Ain't Got Nobody" has a sad blues lyric about loneliness, the music is jaunty and joyful. And jaunty and joyful is what I felt in reading your thoughts about family.

Because as you point out, a family can be created at any time. It doesn't have to be biological. As Werner Erhard says, "In your universe, if LOVE is scarce, WHO isn't creating it?"

I remember when my own life was torn apart by my addiction to alcohol and drugs, and friends and family (understandably) had no interest in interacting with me. I was fortunate enough to find the last ounce of courage left in my system to reach out and ask for help. I ended up in a 12 Step program that not only saved my life but gave me a new kind of family. It was there for me in even more profound and helpful ways than my original family could have been. I regularly went to meetings and created relationships and friendships over the years as I never had before.

That's just one example of how all of us, at any age, can reach out and build a community by caring for others and discovering that doing so returns the blessing many times over. We seniors, especially, need to find just a bit of courage and do that.

It's important not to hide behind the old and false belief, "I prefer to be alone. I don't need to create family and friends." In most cases, this is a rationalization for accepting being pushed to the sidelines. For going along with becoming an afterthought in your existing family. For buying into being a victim of circumstances.

Reacquaint yourself with the many physical, psychological, and spiritual benefits of the new kind of family we have described and get on with creating a well-being community right where you are. Ditch the rationalizations that are keeping you stuck (and possibly sad).

Mindful Choice #9

I will be open-minded and open-hearted about finding collective purpose, support, and joy in the "family" in my life, no matter its derivation.

Conversation Ten
The Search for a Senior "Match"

We discuss senior romance, love, companionship, practical expectations and considerations, and fairly valuing the option of living alone when contemplating a significant relationship later in life.

Will

To add to the earlier comments about my nuclear family, my father left home when he figured out that being married to a woman, despite what my farmer grandparents told him, was not a cure for being gay. At the age of nine, I left home when my mother figured out that I was the one of her four children who was more than she could manage. I moved in with an aunt and uncle in California and lived with them and their three children until I graduated from high school.

Someone with more life experience than me at the time might've predicted that my capacity for identifying and sustaining functional human relationships was going to require some development. They would've been proven right.

I spent about half of my adult years "single." I viewed natural, instinctual attraction as essential for initiating any potential relationship. There were, after all, thousands of years of proof that men and women intuitively knew how to connect by trusting these instincts. In hindsight, many of the connections I made during those years might better be characterized as "encounters" rather than relationships.

Although I didn't think in terms of sustainable relationships, I told myself, "I'm not *not* open to one. Nothing is off the table!" I convinced myself that the statement wasn't *actually* a lie when a natural attraction (and that trusted stirring) was present. Still, when saying goodbye to these many acquaintances in my life, I usually felt blessed by the experience, not disappointed that there wasn't more to come.

In my late 50s and again in my later 60s, I found myself single. I was less active in the real-life social and business worlds than I had been and recognized that I was no longer the "dashing young man" I once may have been. Yet, I was no less interested in having female energy and companionship in my life. What to do?

By then, online dating sites had become an accepted alternative for meeting people in social contexts. Having worked in the information technology sector during most of my career, I was comfortable navigating these sites on the Internet, thereby significantly enlarging the dating pool. Talk about casting a wide "net"!

However, for a man who had lived his romantic life seeking "better love through physical chemistry," I found the online medium lacking: There was no sense of a rocket launching with the inspiring phrase, "We have ignition!!" But I also found it more challenging as an older single to meet people in person.

I have lived alone for over four years, as of this writing. This period has allowed much reflection, including rethinking what course romance as a senior may take. Though I haven't shaken my belief in chemistry, I now know that I cannot divine it through an Internet connection. If you feel cosmic intervention is at work while viewing an online profile, you are projecting hope into someone (or even something) just as likely to be a faker or scammer. If you feel a psychic connection, you are probably alone in that belief.

As I've learned to be comfortably alone as a senior, I offer the following thoughts about personal senior connections:

- People who say, "I'm alone but not lonely," could be kidding themselves. It may be true you are not lonely for a while—even for years. But isolation is not a natural state for most humans. Interaction, relatedness, and being seen, are necessary for optimal functioning and integrated living.
- As seniors, a "failure to thrive" through isolation can manifest in depression and stress (similar to what occurs in infants without human contact). In some cases, this failure can become a downward spiral leading to further withdrawal, more extreme social separation, drug abuse, and even suicide.
- Some make the purposeful choice to live part or even a good portion of their lives alone. It is uncommon, but some choose to live in solitary conditions for a life of contemplation, service, or another purpose. This quiet life can work for those with low requirements for human interaction. In the following quote from Rainer Maria Rilke, a favorite writer of ours, he celebrated this choice: "Solitude is truly an interior affair, and to realize this

insight and to live accordingly amounts to the best and most helpful form of progress."[14]

- Passionate love relies on attraction, which does not typically last beyond the spark storm that opened the relationship. Successful love and romance for older adults are more likely to be centered in the familiarity and comfort of deep friendship, companionship, and mutual understanding, with other elements of intimacy mixed in.[15] This "companionate love" . . . refers to a variety that is durable, slow to develop, and characterized by interdependence and feelings of affection, intimacy, and commitment. Companionate love is also known as affectionate love, friendship-based love, or attachment."[16]

- Companionship later in life also may be more about co-discovering new experiences. Making new choices together can be fresh and liberating. These activities and experiences may include physical activity that can improve the health of both parties: walking, dancing, singing, traveling. Movement and mobility are underrated as reasons to meet and explore with new people.

- It may be more difficult to find senior connections where both parties are willing to allow things to progress naturally—meaning, over time. Our declining lifespans have relevance to this issue, but so does taking time to assure you are giving appropriate consideration to what is in your best interests. There are many ways to "negotiate and configure" relationships to work for the needs of both parties. (Sorry, Steve, I know that sounded like a lawyer, not a modern romantic troubadour!)

- Shared experiences, observations, and mutual learning over years of togetherness formed the baseline for the best of the longer-term relationships I have experienced. So how do seniors reach similar comfort levels and feelings of safety with fewer years to spend together? Embracing understanding, patience, acceptance, and agape (ah-gah-pay) [the form of "love as service"[17]] are all part of it. Simply acknowledging these realities, and trying on different perspectives and possibilities, can open the conversation to creativity and building trust. Many seniors say, "I want my last first date . . ." but should follow the advice "Trust but verify."
- The best way to begin a journey into deep companionship may be to offer support, conversation, and caring to those around you. Rather than withdrawing into isolation, choose to serve others. The energy you create will change the people around you, and they will return energy to you. This energy flow could be fuel for discovering a relationship that might be different from what you experienced in the past. But who's to say you can't experiment—choose red instead of green, bananas rather than strawberries, or a new kind of "connected but independent" relationship?
- There are practical reasons for companionship, too. If someone falls or becomes ill, there is help immediately available to summon first responders. With some sudden onset illnesses or episodes—a stroke or heart attack, for

example—minutes can make the difference between a full recovery and other outcomes.

- Seeking a relationship may appropriately be partly financially driven. "Two incomes are better than one, and we can have the popcorn between us on the couch while we watch reruns. If it is more comfortable (or you snore loudly), you can have your own room too!"
- You needn't wait for companionship to come to you like a thunderbolt from the sky. It is not a form of weakness to seek it out. It is a form of strength manifesting in seeking wellness through relatedness. Don't be afraid to ask others to "keep you in mind" for potential companion prospects.

As older adults, we must rethink caveats like "*If only* he were less talkative, he would be perfect," or "If she would lose some weight, I could really see us together." Although these kinds of hopeful "If only" statements may have been actionable when we were younger, if ever there is a time in life when we must embody the acceptance expressed by, "It is what it is," it has arrived. There will be no straightening of the quite seasoned, double-twist-shaped pretzel of a potential companion without damaging the best of it, should you be unable to accept "what is."

I don't recall who said it, but this applies to all romantic relationships: "I love you for who you are *and* who you are not." "Who you are" and "Who you are not" is established over decades and becomes more entrenched as the years pass. As a take on the Christian marriage vows, these are conditions of "being" that "no man or woman should put asunder"—and in most cases, will be impossible to put asunder!

Steve

Your thoughts are rational, full of common sense, yet accommodate the potential for the magic of chemistry and attraction, too.

What you've written are good guidelines for new relationships. But I have no more guidance to offer about discovering new companions in my life. My wife Kathy and I have been together for more than 30 years, and both of us expect that our "togetherness" will survive (and prosper) until death we do part.

You touched on a life of solitude as a valid choice. But I'd like to offer a bit more on the concept of the "need" for a companion. Being a life coach for many years, one of the many awakenings I've had is, "You don't *need* a romantic partner to have a happy and fulfilling life." And believing that you must have one, while not having it, can lead to deep and unnecessary misery.

I'm not minimizing how nice it is to have a loving partner later in life. It's great! But to believe it's a requirement, or *the* big missing piece when you don't have it, can lead to poor decision-making.

Of course, the false belief that this "need" is based upon is well-established. It was part of our social indoctrination as children, built right into the Western cultural use of the word "love."

Love is almost always related to a romantic partner. Snow White "finds love" after singing, "Someday my prince will come!" Cinderella hums, "so this is love," after just one dance.

The clear message is that without a certain someone, you'll be living a life without love. You will endure a lonely and loveless existence. By mere seconds, you missed the song or the dance that could have saved your life from ruin!

While reading the biography of a powerful woman who was a writer and an activist, I was startled to read near the end of the book that she "finally found love" in her late 60s when she married another author and became his fourth wife. Did she have no experience of love prior to that? Did she not love her life, or her sister, or her dog, or her garden, or her activist cause, or her freedom, or her favorite music, or her writing, or her sweet moments of peace and solitude? Many find these "loves" insufficient for a full life. They fall outside of the "love" defined by our culture (and the advertising industry) and are therefore deficient.

This belief that love only comes from one randomly improbable, perhaps accidental, untrustworthy source (another individual, specific human), is not only ridiculously incorrect, but it leads to an increasing sense of loneliness and despair when that serendipitous bird doesn't land on our head. It also produces superstitious corollaries such as, "I think I just met my soul mate!" and the even sadder, "You complete me!" And remember, this random person is the one in 8,000,000,000 possible Earthly other halves (when you count all sexes).

It *would* be nice to have a wonderful life partner later in life. But to hold your happiness and love of life hostage to making that happen, is a misguided folly destined to become a disappointment. As divorce statistics confirm, you could be even *more* miserable in a partnered state. It could turn out that the old grass was actually greener.

Love is what all of life is made of—not just romance. It's who and what we are. Paradoxically, when that truth is recognized, the chances of having a life partner increase.

I'm not trying to throw cold water on your ideas about finding a later-life companion, Will. I think it's a good and positive idea. But as I think we agree, when a desire for love crosses over from a want to a need, trouble could be in the works. And when people see that clearly, romance can be approached with more adventure and creative fun.

When I first met Kathy over three decades ago, she was in her 30s. I asked her why she had never married or found a life partner. (Back in those olden days that stupid and offensive question was more common, especially from self-proclaimed, closed-minded male traditionalists like me.)

She said, "Why would I need to do that? Life is perfect."

Wow. I was taken aback. She was living "alone" at the time—how could life be perfect? But she pointed out that she had a job she loved, family members she loved, two cats she loved, singing in a choir she loved, and a full life she *loved.*

I wasn't there to "complete" her. Or to make her happy. She was already happy. It seemed I wasn't needed at all. But that actually made our courtship more fun. Fortunately for me, I was wanted—the best status available. And it has made our marriage, and still-developing deep companionship, a rewarding part of my life (and hers, I believe).

I'm also not throwing cold water on people falling in love. That surely happened with Kathy and me, and it continues to bloom. But I am saying that the common sense and thoughtful strategies you offer for finding a partner, Will, are best executed when you choose to see it as a nice-to-have *want* instead of a desperate *need.*

Mindful Choice #10

Deep companionship later in life can be fulfilling in many ways, but I appreciate that my happiness is not contingent upon someone else.

Conversation Eleven
Tapping Your Full Potential

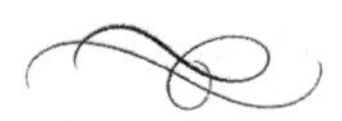

We discuss the psychological shift that is available to view high-performance living as achievable where you are and in everything you do.

Will

A powerfully simple definition of success— "Going as far as you can with all that you've got"—was first introduced to me by a mentor of mine, Larry Wilson. He spent his lifetime as a teacher, corporate trainer, author, and leader, primarily for business teams. He was co-author (with Spencer Johnson) of the original *One-Minute Salesperson*. He founded Wilson Learning Centers in Minnesota, and the Pecos River Learning Center (the latter a challenging outdoor venue near Santa Fe, New Mexico). We met at Pecos River when, as CEO, I took a team of executives from Artisoft there.

We were fortunate to share that time with Lou Holtz, the head football coach of the NCAA national champion University of Notre Dame Fighting Irish. He brought his senior coaching staff to develop potential opportunities for performance improvement within their group. It was a great example of an already highly functioning organization working to squeeze the last bit of "what they've got" to continue achieving at the highest possible level.

Although business and sports teams consist of individuals, we tend to think more about "performance" measured at the company or team level. There is an obvious "bottom line" for each: making a profit or winning a competition. The team's performance, of course, is always based upon the commitment of the individuals to improve their singular contributions for the betterment of the team.

We don't often think to ask ourselves, "Am I living my *life* at the highest level of performance that I can?" Frankly, until now, I had never thought about linking the concepts of "performance" and a "successful life." This inquiry was prompted by my reading an article in the Harvard Business Review entitled "Research: What Do People Need to Perform at a High Level?"[18]

The research was a survey of 14,500 U.S. workers asking them to estimate how much of their full potential they were utilizing in their work. The performance factors sought to be measured by the researchers were at the level of the organization, identifying common factors helping (or hurting) employee effectiveness. Among them were personal characteristics, including mindsets and skills that an individual brings to the job and over which they have some control.

I have taken the liberty of translating the individual characteristics into "high-performance" factors that could be considered in pursuing greater personal well-being. They include:

- *Being able to articulate expectations and objectives* for *improving our physical, psychological, emotional, and spiritual well-being*. Could you write down these expectations and goals right now? What would your life look like if you started each day reminding yourself to notice and even seek out opportunities to perform at a high level in reaching for these objectives—just for the day? What single step could move you to a higher level of well-being?

- *Being curious about what we might do to perform better.* We can read, watch, and listen to expert research, advice, and opinions about the many routes possible to reach for improved well-being. We can ask others what they are doing to improve theirs. Who do you admire for their capability in each of these areas? Inquire about their history, obstacles overcome, and how they sustained their efforts to reach a higher level of mastery. Engaging in this kind of dialogue could enable finding new connections with "high-performance living" as a common interest.
- *Accepting that rules, processes, procedures, and sometimes overcoming bureaucracy are part of the "job" of achieving greater well-being.* Examples include working through the hurdles that are part-and-parcel of the medical establishment: evaluation and testing, repeatedly disclosing and discussing conditions and weaknesses that are highly personal and being patient when confronting poor service and redundancy. The process may be frustrating and, at times, appear impossible. But keeping anxiety at bay will keep you on course and potentially ease the way.
- *Recognizing and rewarding ourselves for reaching new levels of performance, achievement, or personal records.*

Examples include walking two blocks instead of one, losing a pound, reaching out to someone you know is alone, offering to drive an acquaintance to the doctor, forming a bridge group or book club, putting together a small group to plant, and tend to a shared garden. Recognize yourself for these initiatives and praise others too—this can be a powerful motivator. Notice how and where you are bringing the concept of performance into your daily living.

- *Paying attention to shifts in our level of purpose and meaning in daily living.* Maybe get up earlier to give yourself more time to consider, plan, and sharpen your focus on these opportunities in your life. Consider daily journaling or other writing—one method of observing and describing your day-by-day progress in improving your holistic well-being. Pursuing growth and improvement in anything requires keeping the goal front and center and measuring progress.

The researchers also found (in my opinion, unsurprisingly) that an individual's *mindset* about performing at a high level was as necessary as the inputs and guidance from others. For example, some of those surveyed felt better about reaching for higher performance when they viewed their work as a "calling" rather than a "job," recognized this distinction and took pride in it.

What if you took a moment each morning to remind yourself of your "calling" to live your life at the highest level of wellness that you can—again, just for the day? What if you recommitted to *noticing* what is happening with you and around you, just for the day? Become an active observer of your journey and progress. When you adopt "going as far as you can with all that you've got" as the measure of your living "performance," you will *feel* when you are energized and on track—and when you are not.

Steve

I love the choice you are introducing here, Will, because it is counterintuitive for an older person to consider. At age 76, it is unusual and out of the box to ask whether I could perform at a higher level in some area and benefit myself or others. Thank you for raising this exciting concept of "high-performance" as a mindful choice.

Being up for continuous improvement in our daily living goes against the mythology that says aging means we must act like old men and old women— "age-appropriately old" as determined by . . . nobody seems to know! Unfortunately, many of us willingly accept the elapsed time since our birth as a reason to give up on the concepts of excellence and performing well. Even semi-retirement means, "Give me a break, cut me some slack, I'm not the person I used to be . . . as you can see, I'm older now. Why do you think I bought this deluxe power recliner?"

Recently I watched Phil Mickelson win the PGA Championship at the age of 50—the oldest golfer ever to win a major tour title. He played against much younger players on a very long course that required enormous physical and mental stamina. The younger superstars interviewed after the tournament looked worn out and exhausted.

Phil had played a little bit on the PGA Senior Tour for older golfers but also had recently chosen to bring his performance up to its highest possible level. His diet, including some fasting, intensive exercise, and total focus on sharpening his skills, was something younger golfers would do while trying to break into the professional ranks. At Phil's age, no one expected him to make this kind of effort. But he showed up trimmer and physically stronger than he ever was in his early career, and he shocked the golf world by decisively winning one of the premier golf tournaments of the year.

You may be thinking that the age of 50 isn't all that old. And almost anyone can still play golf at 50. But we're not talking about just playing golf. We're talking about a major professional tournament. And more importantly, we're talking about ignoring your numerical age and choosing to bring high-performance to a physically and mentally challenging activity. The odds against Phil winning were so great that the television commentators were calling him an "antiquity."

The choice to perform at a higher level in old age is even more fun than during our ambitious, youthful years because it surprises people. You can do it for self-satisfaction and pure joy.

But it can't be done at all without first *noticing* the opportunity for making an effort.

Higher performance can be applied to little things, too. It doesn't have to be a major golf tournament. When our dishwasher broke down at the beginning of the COVID lockdown, I took on the chore of washing the dishes by hand every night. I started out doing it half-heartedly and reluctantly. It was, after all, merely a task to get out of the way. But soon, Kathy noticed that some of the plates and glasses weren't as spotless as she would like. My opinion was that they were "clean enough," and if a do-over was required now and then, no big deal.

Then an idea hit me—and this was before I saw what you wrote about high-performance. I would treat this dishwashing and drying like a contest and up my game. I took more time. I engaged my pride. I washed and washed, rinsed and dried, then held each dish, glass, pot, and utensil up to the light as if I were in a televised tournament getting the award for having the cleanest dishes. I began to love it. I looked forward to doing the dishes and doing them the best they could be done!

I chose a higher level of performance just for the fun of it, in an activity that would be recognized and celebrated by few.

I did the same thing with a song I had agreed to perform for a wedding reception. My friends and family would have been perfectly okay with a medium to low level of musical performance. They would have said, "That was touching. He's still pretty good. But not like he was a few years ago. Bless his heart. It's the thought that really matters." But instead, I took extra voice lessons, rehearsed incessantly, and gave the performance my all.

I'm not pointing these things out to brag about me. I'm far too prone to ignore and not even want to notice places where better and higher performance could be an option. (Which is almost everywhere and in everything.) Most of my attitude was that good enough is good enough, with a silent whisper to myself, "*…especially given my age.*"

This notion of *high-performance aging* is very provocative, Will. I appreciate your challenge.

Mindful Choice #11

I choose to live a high-performance life, going as far as I can with all I've got in whatever I am doing.

Conversation Twelve
Your Outer Wrapper

We offer observations about the changes in our physical incarnations through years of living, and their relationship to our true Spirit.

Will

Aging is a gradual process that allows us to slip from one year to the next without recognizing the changes in how we appear to the world. For most, this is the case through youth and young adulthood—for some, maybe even middle age.

Then, boom! One day, we notice undeniable changes—clear evidence of aging—in the appearance of the vessel we have occupied for all our life.

You see the reflection of someone you might once have described as "old," or at least older than you. You do a doubletake: "Who IS that?" "When did THAT happen?" "This is NOT me!"

We may attempt to "reverse" the unwelcome look, at least for a while. As a woman or man, we may reach for hair dye, wigs, Botox, facial fillers, makeup, skin rejuvenators, bra-stuffers (not most men), even plastic surgery. *If only* we could get our external reflection back into alignment with our internal image of ourselves. This is important to our self-esteem! "People" must be thinking, "She used to seem so vivacious." "I thought he was much younger. He's actually old and looks it." "I hadn't seen them for a couple of years, and I didn't recognize either one of them!"

We may have noticed and reluctantly accepted these kinds of changes where only we could see them (especially the parts strategically covered by clothing). But when they finally register as visible to the world, an alarm goes off. It could be that in the rushing river that is life today, we haven't squeezed in any time for reflection on the predictable passages of a lifetime and how these eventually show up in our appearances.

In truth, through our denials and protests, we are perpetuating the cultural myth that aging is about deterioration, decay, and loss. And look who is confirming the myth and trying to run from it! We are suffering from a lifetime of brainwashing that the only life stage of value is youth—and we no longer look like them. We ourselves are among those throwing ageist rocks at the parade of souls moving through life. And we are all in the parade! Ouch.

I knew a man, Steve Patterson, whose life and death brought this into clear view for me. He played for Coach John Wooden and the UCLA Bruins men's basketball team. He started at the center position after the departure of Kareem Abdul Jabbar (formerly known as Lew Alcindor) and before the arrival of Bill Walton. While they were there, he backed them up. Steve and Kareem each earned three NCAA championship rings, and Bill, two. Steve went on to play in the NBA for a few years, with the Cleveland Cavaliers and the Chicago Bulls.

I didn't know Steve personally when he was a basketball

player; I met him and his wife, Carlette, after he had turned 50. However, by the spring of 2004 we had become friends. I soon learned that Steve had told Carlette he had been experiencing back pain for a couple of months and was increasingly uncomfortable. He thought it was a function of being 6’ 9” and somewhat in the decline of a vigorous youth.

Following a visit to the doctor and a battery of tests, the diagnosis was lung cancer. He was 55 and had never smoked a day in his life.

It was quickly apparent that the course of the disease was advanced and that any cure would be miraculous. Although Steve had faith in God that such a miracle would occur, he died six weeks to the day from his diagnosis.

I went to the memorial service at the church he attended, including hundreds of adults and about 30 children. It was a beautiful celebration of his life in prayer, praise, and song. Toward the end of the service, the pastor asked all the children to come forward. He gave wrapped pieces of hard candy to each of them. Then he said,

> I know that you are feeling sadness today. And being sad is okay. It is part of letting go of someone who has passed on. Just like the paper around this piece of candy, Steve’s body was his wrapper. It protected what was inside—the good part—the part that mattered most. When we die, it means that our body has served its purpose. It can be left behind, just like the wrapper from the candy. Steve has left his physical body behind—it didn’t work anymore. But his soul left his body, and the memory of his presence and goodness was released to us forever.

At that moment, I realized that wishing for the state of our "wrappers" to stay the same was overlooking the obvious. Of course, time will affect the condition of the wrapper. But the goodness is inside, and that part can grow, and get stronger, richer, and more powerful with age. Those willing to look inside, will see and experience it. This is the potential for older adults traversing the second half of life. This is the inner journey that is open to us now—the one that can define us as beings beyond how our containers look to others (and to us). The one that we have time and energy for now.

"Thoroughly unprepared, we take the step into the afternoon of life. Worse still, we take this step with the false presupposition that our truths and our ideals will serve us as hitherto. But we cannot live the afternoon of life according to the program of life's morning; for what was great in the morning will be little at evening, and what in the morning was true, will at evening have become a lie."

~ Carl Jung

Now, you can like your wrapper or not, but as we will talk about a bit later, you should keep it functioning as well as possible for as long as you can. Ultimately its value is as a container for the "you" that is making your way through this world. It is the lamp for your Light which shines the way to your inner "good stuff."

Steve

It took me many years—decades—to fully realize that although I *have* a body, I am *not* my body. There's so much more than that to me and everyone else.

Once I realized that, it became apparent that the quality of my life is more important than how I look along the way. Pursuit of the appearance of youth can result in desperate (and sometimes visually disturbing) attempts to hang on to yesterdays that have passed. They weren't actually lost but they can't be found (recaptured) either.

My body is merely an instrument, although an important one. As St. Francis of Assisi said, "Lord, make me an instrument of your peace. Where there is hatred, let me sow love . . ." Like the notes from a clarinet or saxophone, the notes of creativity, love, and compassion pass through our bodies and are released to the world, not stored in our physical state.

John Keats was one of the world's most celebrated poets whose work has endured and will likely live on forever. The last line from his "Ode on a Grecian Urn" was, "Beauty is truth. Truth is beauty. That is all you know on Earth and all you need to know." It is still quoted the world over.

Keats was 25 years old when he died. His body left us too quickly, but his truth and beauty live on. Not because he lived longer and looked good doing it, but because he *expressed himself.* He wrote of truth and beauty while he had the opportunity and released it to the world.

Overidentification with our bodies has many consequences. Aging movie stars, celebrities, and even some of our neighbors go through surgeries and other bodily manipulations (and not always successfully) in an attempt to appear as they did when *they* viewed themselves at their peak.

When we, in our society, check in with older people to see how they are "feeling," we are almost always asking for a medical report—about the arthritis, the recent hip replacement, and any other bodily breakdowns or ailments du jour. This reinforces the mythology that the body is the be-all and end-all. Back and forth—they hear it from us, and then we hear it back from them.

What are we really asking, truth be told? It isn't, "How are you feeling about the life you are leading?" It's, "How are you faring today with the aging process and your body breaking down?" The more that the discomfort is discussed and highlighted, the greater becomes the biological identity assumed by some older adults.

But as spiritual teachers have been saying for thousands of years—and as quantum physicists and neuroscientists are discovering—the body is merely a vehicle to be temporarily used by the soul, spirit, and divine consciousness that make up who we really are. Merely a vessel, as you said, Will, for "…the good stuff inside!"

And yet, we certainly don't treat it like that. I never called my grandfather to find out how his car was, whether he had changed the oil or if the brakes were still squeaking. But I always asked about his physical body as if it were him. I cared about him. But at some unspoken level, he must have known I was leaving him out of every conversation.

The body, like one's car, certainly ought to be cared for if we are to live our best life during the graciously gifted "rest of our days." And I'm not suggesting that concern for an elderly loved one's health is a misuse of compassion.

I'm just saying, in my opinion, and through my own spiritual and psychological experience, it is a misplaced and limiting belief that the body and its linear existence on Earth are the Holy Grail. That belief is the source of much of our psychological misery, especially in our later years.

Mindful Choice #12

I will age gracefully and without apology on the outside and will strive to become complete, wise, and soul-centered on the inside.

Conversation Thirteen
Normal Aging—Everything is Connected

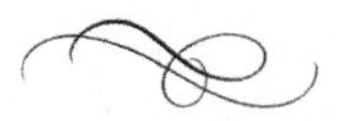

We explore some of the effects of a typical aging process, the opportunities to slow them down and restore lost capacity, and once again underscore the incredible value of awareness.

Will

When your doctor says, "You are aging normally!" you might breathe a sigh of relief. Then, feeling more relaxed, you might not ask the next question, "Doctor, what does normal aging mean?"

One doctor put it in simple terms for me. "Consider that you own a car with 100,000 miles on it. If the mechanic tells you, it is in normal condition for the make, model, and mileage, you will probably feel good about it. It's the same with your body. In your case, you are aging normally for a person of your year of birth, which means, just as with your car, you are doing well given your mileage and normal wear-and-tear." When hearing it put this way, it might be easy to walk out of the exam room, turn the ignition, and drive it some more "miles."

Not so fast, though. Let's look at what's behind the curtain of "normal" aging.

The descriptions below are available in a simple online Google search and aren't necessarily groundbreaking. After reading them, I said to myself, "Too much information!" as well as "...and no surprises." [Steve and I are neither medical professionals nor experts, so please talk with one if you have questions about or concerns with what you read here.]

In the spirit of lifting our collective knowledge, let's look at some of the physiological changes typically associated with aging and their consequences.[19,20]

Your *heart* must work harder due to the stiffening of arteries and blood vessels. This can make certain physical activities (e.g., strenuous exercise, long walks, and climbing stairs and hills) more difficult.

Due to loss of elasticity, *skin* wrinkles and may bruise more readily.

Bones shrink and become less dense, and therefore more fragile and delicate. We may notice we seem shorter than we once were, and it is likely true. Beginning in our 40s, we could lose one to two inches in height over the rest of our lives.

Muscles are also affected. Most of us will experience losses of strength, flexibility and endurance over time. Muscle mass decreases three to five percent every decade, starting at about 40. Over 60, this rate increases.

Older adults who lose some *mobility* are less likely to remain living at home and have higher incidences of disease, disability, and hospitalization. In general terms, loss of mobility directly leads to a lower quality of life. Related to mobility, the increasing incidence of sedentarism (sitting too much) is a growing health concern. As mentioned in Conversation Two, the four-and-a-half hours per day that a typical senior watches television contributes.

Some of the most annoying and prevalent changes occur in *seeing* and *hearing*. Vision changes can include far-sightedness, a result of the hardening of the lens. In addition, cataracts, a clouding of the lens, may develop. This can cause blurry vision and sometimes blindness if not treated. When it comes to hearing, following conversations in a crowded room or hearing sounds at high frequencies may become difficult.

These points aren't intended to be a comprehensive recap but simply a reminder: Aging has physical consequences that are unavoidable. We all will inevitably experience some or all the typical indicators of aging. However, at what age and to what degree these occur will depend in part on how well we care for our bodies. Many conditions can be improved or lessened with your commitment to achieving the highest degree of wellness possible.

Going back to the car analogy, normal aging is within a range. Some vehicles age better, and some worse. If we treat our cars as "old clunkers," they will probably return the favor. Lack of maintenance, care, and regular attention will cause our vehicles to age faster than is necessary. Try not changing the oil for 20,000 miles, don't keep the radiator full of fluid, or don't bother to replace the tires.

With our physical "vehicles," the same logic applies. If we treat them as "old and tired" and not worthy of the most basic attention, we will likely see atrophy and decline earlier and faster than expected. We will continue to discuss opportunities for improvement and extension of our "healthspan"[21] in the coming conversations.

Steve

A while back, I decided to just give in to the breakdowns and deteriorations you describe here, Will, attributing it to "normal" aging. I said to myself, "Just live with it." Maybe take a Zen or spiritual approach and just rest in total acceptance of the decline, or even meditate on the natural beauty of impermanence and decay. Like the autumn leaves red and gold. Just see it as the Tao or the natural way of things. *Acceptance of decay as the way!* Or, if I am evolving enough spiritually through prayer and meditation, I could even welcome my physical deterioration!

But I did nothing, as you say, to "counter" any of this.

Then, upon reading your book *Untethered Aging*,[22] I realized that I really could have the rest of my years be my best years ever. I could make this happen, especially if I were to increase my creative activity, both physical and mental. To leave the "acceptance as the way" approach for when I actually pass away and leave my "wrapper" behind.

So, I scouted around for other books on aging—specifically those exploring the effects exercise and conscious breathing have on an older person's brain and the body. (In other words, me.)

I dove in, and of the many books I found, the most inspiring was *The Real Happy Pill*: *Power Up Your Brain by Moving Your Body*. It was written by Anders Hansen who is a physician and psychiatry specialist from Sweden's Karolinska Institute.

I experienced a genuine "wow!" factor throughout the book, especially the section on the positive effects exercise has on the brain's capacity for creativity, a favorite subject of mine. As you can see, I'm still writing books and want to continue doing that. But, during the completion of my last book, I experienced a diminishing mental capacity for writing. I was worried about it but wrote it off as "aging."

But Dr. Hansen was persuasive about the brain's ability to retain great creative power at any age if we integrate physical exercise into our daily regimen. So, I began brisk walking each day. I also started lifting light weights, doing yogic balancing, and deep breathing. Initially, I did this to test the neurological and biological studies Dr. Hansen reveals in his book.

However, it was only about a week and a half before I started noticing significant improvements in my cognitive function. My thinking became clearer, and my imagination started coming back to where it was in my younger years when my books seemed to just flow out of me.

And then there was the title of his book: *The Real Happy Pill.* The part I'd been most skeptical about was happiness itself. Obviously, it is the crucial element to having my last years be my best. And, to my great surprise, my low moods started to occur less often, and my spirits rose. Just by moving my body more!

I'd started to feel like the old Sinatra song, "Young at Heart." I used to think that song was a kind of unrealistic, blue-sky fantasy. But now the lyrics meant more, such as the last verse, "And if you should survive to a hundred and five / Think of all you'll derive out of being alive / and here is the best part / you'll have a head start / if you are among the very young at heart."

Now, I have no real interest in reaching my 105th birthday. Being young at heart for me is only valuable if it's happening in the here and now. Who knew the simplicity of moving one's body more and breathing more consciously would have such an immediate impact on someone like me, a man in his mid-70s?

Many people I know who are near my age turn to pharmaceutical help for mood and cognition and are willing to live with the side effects. I'm not against that when it's the only alternative. But I'm glad I looked into the organic choice of essential exercise and breathing with greater consciousness.

One final point about Dr. Anders' book: It is not just for the elderly. I even sent a copy to my grandson, who is a musician and songwriter. His mood and creativity will greatly benefit if he is willing to apply what he reads.

And, for the record, Will, I continue to appreciate your setting up the research and facts for us through your deep curiosity. It is a vital part of keeping this conversation real and true.

Will

Even if I wanted to, or occasionally apologize for it, I can't and don't want to stop being curious. Sometimes I go down rabbit holes chasing one thing and discover something completely different. But often what I learn in that random digging is even more fascinating than what I started looking for. So, then I pursue *that* for a while until it takes me to something new. I am always surprised to see the connections that exist, click by click, no matter where I began.

As I move from site to site, topic to topic, point to point—there is always something linking them. I began to examine my role in this process. In each instance, my unique perspective and attention are acting upon what otherwise is inert information. I see, extract, and take away what is relevant for me. My journeys are not random because I am the viewer, actor, catalyst, and connector.

For the same reason, even the starting point isn't random—*I* see something that triggers action. But if I don't consciously bring my perspective and curiosity to the information, nothing changes in it, or me for that matter.

The key is to notice those connections, to bring a conscious, focused attention to them. The degree or intensity of our attention determines how we experience what we are engaging with in the now of the moment. It is turning awareness and consciousness into action through the application of our attention (and minimizing distractions).[23] It is a bit like learning to drive. There are many distractions, but we learn to see and act on what we need to see to safely navigate.

Your comments reminded me that last year when I was writing *Untethered Aging*, you sent me a link to a Mindvalley.com video talk by brainiac Tom Chi: "Everything is Connected: Here's How." He offers a science-based string of connections that shows how parts of every human's mineral composition can only have originated from essential elements in the Universe that are billions of years old.

You described recently noticing a partial decline in your ability to write efficiently and creatively. What you did once you noticed was another proof that awareness is the starting point for discovering a string of connections that lead to answers.

Here is my playback of what happened. Noticing your creative challenge *connected* to your decision to learn more about improving your brain function. Your seeking of that information *connected* you with the book, *The Real Happy Pill*. By reading it, you were *connected* to knowledge about the linkages between physical exercise, brain function, and creativity. This information was *connected* to motivating you to walk, lift some light weights, and work on your balance and mobility. The actions you took to get into motion were *connected* to rapid improvements in your ability to create with greater clarity, which was what started the process in the first place.

All those connections meant you could continue to work with your coaching clients, inspire and entertain your readers, and interact with others in the world in the ways that you had always been able to do. AND because of your noticing and taking the first actions, followed by the rapid sequencing of those connections, the elapsed time between noticing the problem and seeing the beginnings of a solution was less than two weeks. This is a single illustration of the power of energetic connections.

The noticing of the effects of aging can lead to connections to solutions for any senior, even when a belief exists that there was no choice but to accept them. Mindful choices (first illuminated by noticing the condition or a change) can immediately lead to small actions that can be taken. Just as happened with you, Steve, these choices can yield enormous improvements in anyone's quality of life.

In your case, other than the cost of the book, the rest was free. No fancy equipment, diet supplements, or an expensive pilgrimage to Tibet were required. Your almost immediate return on a simple decision and a small investment of time is an example for all of us.

Your age didn't keep you from recapturing something important to your desired state of wellness. To that point, *not noticing* was holding you back. Once you became aware of it, and then took a single step toward learning, a sequence of connections was revealed that led to a solution.

Everything is connected. Our bodies to our minds to our attitudes to our energy to our spirituality and our souls. As holistic humans, small changes can yield significant shifts in the quality of our lives. You can create a new "normal" in its best version by noticing and then taking actions—even if they are small ones.

Mindful Choice #13

I will raise my awareness of small changes in my physical, mental, psychological, and spiritual health, and take action in my best interest to improve my quality of life.

Conversation Fourteen

Our Bodies Want to Be Well

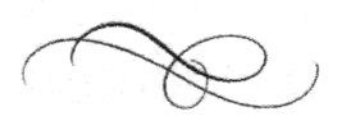

We offer the uncomfortable truth about the neglect and active abuse of our bodies, the stress and pain of everyday living, and the impact of the loneliness epidemic.

Will

Sharing facts with our readers is one of the foundations for all our conversations. It provides a context for considering what we have to say about the subject at hand and for weighing the relative value of our suggested mindful choices.

Because many facts are not uplifting, I am sometimes asked, "Why do you put that downer material in your writing? Man, nobody wants to read that s@#t! I feel bad enough already." Despite the resistance, in our heart of hearts we know that facts don't care how they make us feel. If we don't know the truth—even if it is depressing—we are ignoring key ingredients for making things different.

We live in a world with rapid and extraordinary change, significant and sometimes perplexing diversity, and simultaneously occurring disruptive influences, among many other forces. As a result, individually and collectively, we experience persistent feelings of fear, uncertainty, and doubt.

It's no wonder that there is an underlying sense of pain that often manifests itself in stress, depression, and other mental health challenges, all across our nation.

Majority of Americans Have Struggled With Mental Health

% of U.S. respondents who have experienced the following mental health issues in the past 12 months

Issue	%
Anxiety	41%
Stress	39%
Depressive phase	30%
Feeling of loneliness/social isolation	28%
Mood swing	26%
Phases of sadness	23%
Panic attacks	20%
Struggles with self-esteem	20%
Phases of lethargy	14%
Phobias	8%
None of the above	26%

3 in 10 Americans said that the pandemic has had a negative effect on their mental health

Based on an online survey of 2,049 U.S. adults conducted between July 26 and August 10, 2021
Source: Statista Global Consumer Survey

statista

The facts about our collective well-being are not always pretty. Even the financial facts we will share with you in Conversation Twenty-One "The (Not So Secret) Secret to

Financial Sufficiency" are, to me, surprising and uncomfortable in their pervasiveness. The numbers seem to belie what we see (or think we see) all around us: The American Dream, happily and successfully pursued by everyone from sea to shining sea!

Our "normal" has gradually become something that many don't want to look at too closely. In many cases, viewing the "mainstream" reality can be disturbing—even shocking. However, there could be a sense of relief in knowing that the pain we feel individually is the sense of the majority. We believe there is little value in offering mindful choices for improved well-being if there is not a clear picture of what being "normal" represents.

"Before the truth sets you free, it tends to
make you miserable."
~ Richard Rohr

We are committed to doing more than saying, "Here is the terrible news—thanks for reading!" without offering choices for well-being for the better. After all, our conversations are about making mindful choices for improved living and happiness.

Steve

I'm with you on this, Will. One thing Nathaniel Branden used to say to the people he was counseling (including me) on the benefits of facing the facts and waking up to reality was, "You can't leave a place you've never been." In other words, you can't make anything better if you don't know what your starting point is.

The GOOD NEWS is that most of us start with a healthy body. About ninety-nine percent of us are born in what you could call "near-perfect" condition. Healthy and ready for life.[24] Our bodies come equipped with the ability to immediately defend against many diseases, heal themselves, and sometimes even recover from death. (As you know, I am fascinated by the insights offered by survivors of near-death experiences. We will talk about this in our final conversation, "Surviving Death.")

But our bodies don't come with an operating manual or a warranty, nor do parents receive the crayon version of how to maintain their child's health in its initial, pristine state. Thus begins the onslaught of imperfect care and feeding, and with few exceptions, it never ends.

Will

The average age of onset of most chronic diseases that represent the leading causes of death is often before 50 and sometime younger.

Age of Onset of Select Chronic Diseases[25]

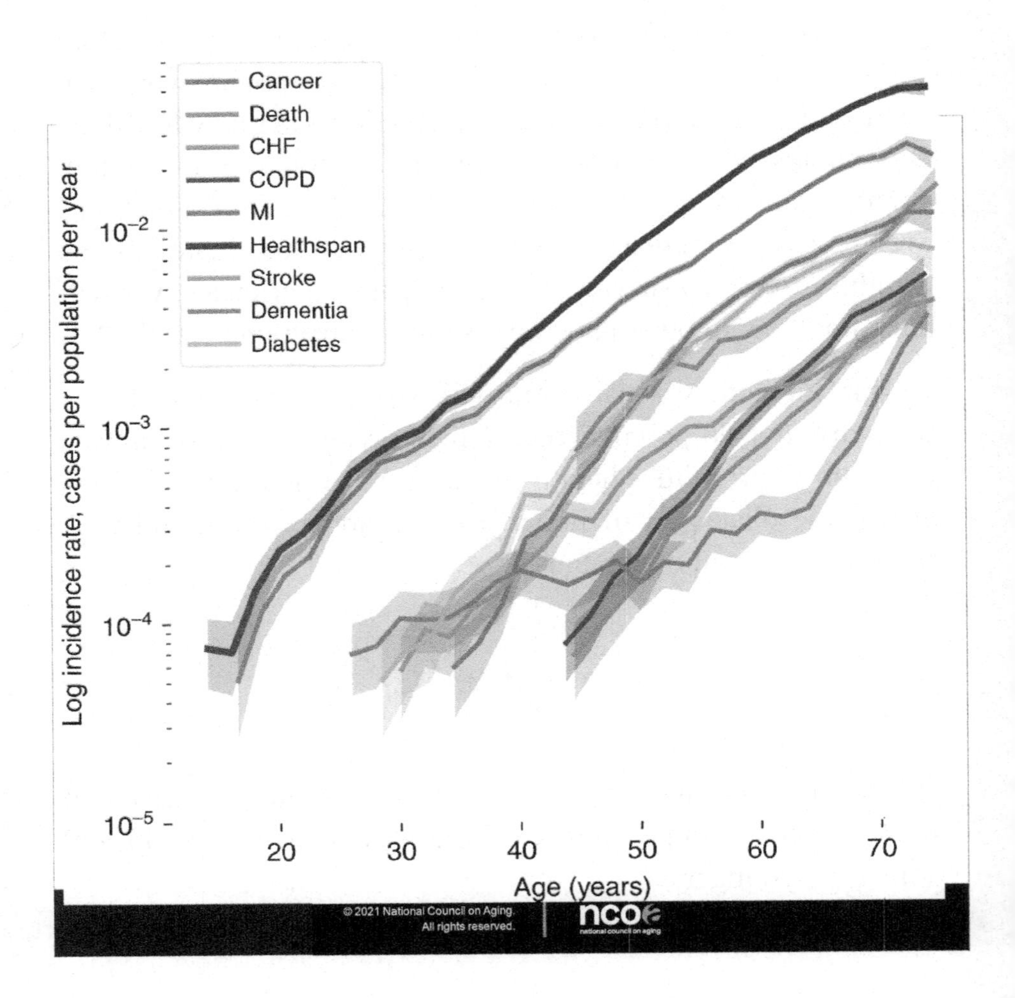

Eighty percent of adults over 65 are dealing with at least one chronic condition and over two-thirds have two or more.

Between 1950 and 2010, life expectancy rose from about 68 to over 78, increasing 8.5 percent in a single generation. But, in 2010, in the immediate aftermath of the Great Recession, the life expectancy curve flattened for the first time in six decades.

Despite spending more on health care than any other country, the United States has seen increasing mortality and falling life expectancy for people ages 25 to 64, typically the prime of life. According to the report "Life Expectancy and Mortality Rates in the United States, 1959-2017,"[26] by 2014, average life expectancy began to fall due to death rates from suicide, drug overdoses, liver disease, and dozens of other causes involving younger and middle-aged adults.

I see this as evidence of the pervasive lack of purpose, loneliness, and pain—across all age groups—that has inexorably become the norm in our country. Ellen Meara, a professor and health economist at the Dartmouth Institute for Health Policy and Clinical Practice, comments that, "the report reveals a broad erosion in health, with no single 'smoking gun.' There's something more fundamental about how people are feeling at some level — whether it's economic, whether it's stress, whether it's deterioration of family," she said. "*People are feeling worse about themselves and their futures, and that's leading them to do things that are self-destructive and not promoting health.*"[27] [Emphasis added.]

David Leonhardt in *The New York Times*, "The Morning,"[28] wrote,

> It's hard to imagine a more alarming sign of a society's well-being than an inability to keep its citizens alive . . . For many, daily life lacks the structure, status and meaning that it once had . . . Many people feel less of a connection to an employer, a labor union, a church or community groups. They are less likely to be married. They are more likely to endure chronic pain and to report being unhappy . . . Other health problems,

> including diabetes and strokes, have also surged among the working class.

Our lifestyle choices have an enormous impact on our health and well-being: poor diet, stress, smoking, drinking alcohol excessively, illegal drug use, physical inactivity, and chronic disease. These and other "failures to cope" with the reality of living in our cultural and social blur—have led to rising "deaths of despair."[29]

We are often unwilling to make small changes that could raise our level of well-being, help us feel better and live longer in a happier state. Instead, we justify self-destructive behaviors and perpetuate them through a never-ending stream of reasons, excuses, and rationalizations. Our bodies want to be well, but we override nature's wishes. We may loudly state our intention to "try" to change (and join a chorus of millions)—but simply don't, or don't sustain it for long.

Accepting this course of unmindful living, often without any resistance, indicates immaturity when it comes to responsible self-care. It also reveals the presence of widespread unrealistic expectations about the more significant, mindful effort required of us to stay well, especially in the second half or last third or quarter of life.

We are "owed" nothing in this world, including indestructible bodies, yet the denial of this truth seems to be the rule for many American adults. We must work at being well, which includes self-restraint from what can make us vulnerable to unwellness.

Many people of all ages have elected to destroy the vessel taking them through life. Sometimes, that choice is more active, such as excessive smoking or drinking, or abusing prescription opioids. Sometimes it is passive, such as poor diet and lack of exercise. The data suggest that as a consequence of unmindful living, the underlying mental and physical health of a large fraction of the population is declining. How did we get to the point where the *pain of living* overwhelms an interest in, let alone a genuine desire for, wellness?

This may have been a rant, Steve, but seriously, what gives?

Steve

That was a gut punch, Will. When you dive into the watery depths of reality, you come up with things that everyone should know but many have avoided due to the pain of confronting them.

I cringed while reading what you've laid out—because it's confirmed by just looking around me. The sacred gifts of our life form were provided to enjoy life with, not destroy. Not all of us, but I'll say most, neglect or actively abuse our bodies.

So why do we do that?

I'll give you my personal answer.

In my 20s and 30s, I abused my body with drugs and alcohol to the point of life-threatening, near-suicidal addiction. At the time, I didn't accept the fact that it was abusive behavior. It just felt like some kind of relief—a way to jump-start what had become a depressingly dead soul: mine.

I was, in the words of the great country song by Johnny Lee, "Looking for love in all the wrong places." Not believing for a moment that long-term happiness and inner spiritual peace were possible, I grabbed any short-term pleasure or relief or boost I could get, even knowing that the hangovers and crashes sure to come would be painful. I said, "So what? Life sucks, and then you die."

I won't go much further down that biographical road in this conversation. I wrote a whole book about it called *Death Wish*. Despite the unfortunate title, it was my account of how *great* (ultimately) it was to go through a complete physical and spiritual recovery from addiction and alcoholism, then create a new life as a result. Especially when, this time, I learned how to look for love and peace and joy in all the *right* places.

It's no accident that alcohol has been called "spirits." It's an attempt to get something good from alcohol that can really only come from a different kind of "Spirit." Booze has also been called "false courage," which is entirely accurate. Alcohol and drugs are false everything. False joy, false freedom, false peace, false bravado, false love of life. It's not only false, but it's agonizingly temporary! (At least in my experience and the experience of my many friends who go to support meetings to continue working through spiritual recovery programs.)

Gordon Patrick Boyce writes a blog on Thailand's HOPE Rehab website called *The Addiction Complex*. In it, he wrote, "During the formation of Alcoholics Anonymous, Bill Wilson, one of AA's founding members, was in correspondence with [the legendary psychologist] Carl Jung. Jung asserted that the alcoholic's craving was, '… the equivalent, on a low level, of the spiritual thirst of our being wholeness expressed in medieval language: the union with God.' Jung stated that what an addict or alcoholic pursues in drugs or alcohol—a wholeness of being—actually can be found in becoming spiritually connected. Instead of looking on the outside for wholeness, go within."

There you go. It's not just me; it's Carl Jung, too. Yes, these self-inflicted physical ailments that you've laid out for us, Will, are part of the body connection, but most of the solutions also belong with "Spirit." This is the unavoidable connectedness and harmony within our Universe, as we discussed in Conversation Seven.

This concept represented one more enlightened shift for me in my gratefully recovered years after addiction. While life's most important choices can be neatly divided into the categories of mind, body, and spirit, the ultimate solutions almost always require all three elements working together.

We can choose to commit from this day forward to simply offer mindful respect and gratitude for our health and strength, and never stop asking for experienced outside help in how best to do it.

Will

Thank you for candidly offering the benefit of your direct experience, along with the hope represented by your remarkable transformation. I had never considered craving drugs or alcohol as "a thirst for wholeness." It opens a whole new dimension for rationalizing abuse. "I'm not drunk; I'm on a spiritual journey!" But I am a long-term follower of Jungian points of view, and I'll take it to heart.

To indelibly make this point, over just 18 years (from 1999 to 2017), the number of alcohol-related deaths in the U.S. doubled to more than 70,000. Cirrhosis, irreversible scarring of the liver, has many causes, including alcohol consumption, obesity, nonalcoholic fatty liver disease, and hepatitis. From 1999 to 2016, annual cirrhosis deaths increased by 65 percent, to 34,174, according to a study published in the journal *BMJ*. The most significant increases were related to alcoholic cirrhosis among people ages 25 to 34 years old.[30] By 2030, deaths due to cirrhosis are projected to triple.

Any substance capable of being used to the point of abuse has found new users—and keeps chronic abusers on the hook. The use and abuse of opioids and other drugs has skyrocketed. More than 93,000 Americans died of drug overdoses last year,[31] the highest number of such deaths in a single year.

I believe that loneliness is at the root of many behaviors that put us at risk. The feeling of loneliness has reached an all-time high, with nearly half of the 20,000 U.S. adults surveyed by Cigna reporting they sometimes or always feel alone.[32] In addition, forty percent of survey participants reported they sometimes or always feel that their relationships are not meaningful and cause them to feel isolated. The most recent U.S. Census data show that more than a quarter of the population lives alone—the highest rate ever recorded. In addition, more than half of the population is unmarried, and marriage rates and the number of children per household have declined over the past ten years.

When you apply the percentages relating to loneliness and isolation from the Cigna report to the total U.S. adult population, *100 to 125 million of us sometimes or always feel isolated* or alone.

Given the pervasiveness of loneliness and the range of resulting adverse outcomes, perhaps each of us could reach out and positively embrace and engage with just one person. I believe that such a gesture could significantly improve wellness among our citizens.

You can change someone's life by seeing them as valuable in this world. And to acknowledge them, you simply have to be a human, not a psychiatrist or medical professional. Consider it a "wellness" or "life" watch, through which you extend your humanity and empathy to another. In a culture with runaway loneliness as a part of it, that single choice could enrich and even lengthen the game of life for many.

Mindful Choice #14

I choose to commit to healthful living and raise my awareness of how I may be neglecting or abusing my body. I will pay my personal commitment forward by selecting one or more fellow humans for a "wellness watch."

Conversation Fifteen
The Pain of Gain

We reveal the startling truth of an overweight population, obesity as a cultural norm, the rising incidence of related chronic diseases, and shorter, less healthy life expectancies.

Will

The average woman in the United States now weighs as much as a man half a century ago. Men, on average, now weigh about 30 pounds more than they did back then. Seventy-two percent of the adult American population is overweight (having a BMI [body mass index] of 25+).

According to the National Institute of Health, a BMI of:

- Less than 18.5 means that a person is underweight.
- Between 18.5 and 24.9 is ideal.
- Between 25 and 29.9 is overweight.
- Thirty or higher indicates obesity.

The United States has the highest rate of obesity among developed countries.[33] Obesity among U.S. adults ages 20 through 74 has risen from less than 11 percent in 1960 to over 45 percent currently.

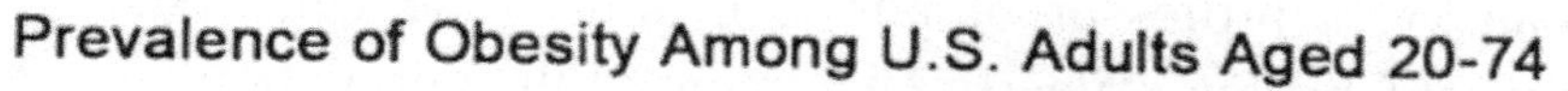

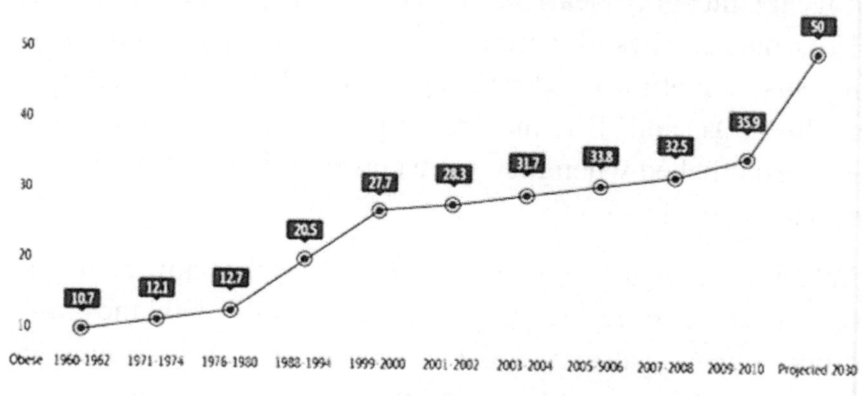

Derived from NHANES data (http://www.cdc.gov/nchs/data/hestat/obesity_adult_09_10/obesity_adult_09_10.html#table1)

Using current trends from each state, researchers project that by 2030 one in two adults in the U.S. will be considered obese, and one in four will be *considered severely obese* (the latter having a BMI of 40 and higher).[34]

Obesity rates by state, 2030 (projected)

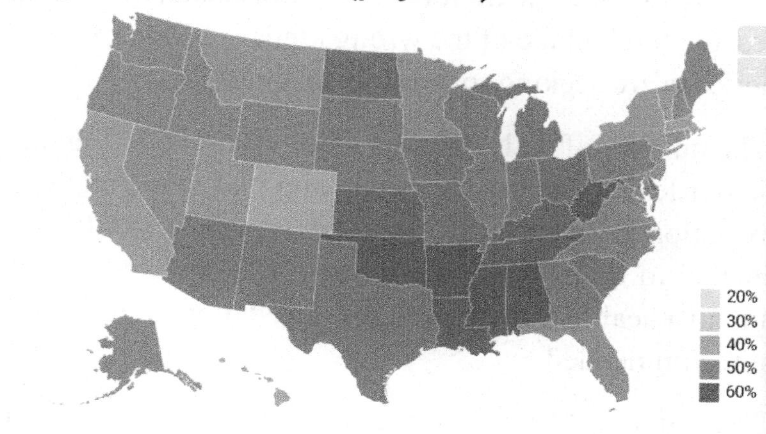

Obesity is defined as a BMI over 30

Map: Elijah Wolfson for TIME • Source: N Engl J Med 2019;381:2440-50. • Created with Datawrapper

Obesity is also rising in children. According to Jay

Olshansky, a professor of public health at the University of Illinois at Chicago, "Nearly 19 percent of the population ages 2 to 19 is obese. These kids are acquiring obesity in their early teen years, sometimes under the age of ten. When they get into their 20s, 30s, and 40s, they're carrying the risk factors for obesity established when they were children. We didn't see that in previous generations."

When it comes to weight gain, the issue is the same as it has always been. People are eating more calories than they are burning. Excess caloric intake is one of the chief ways we degrade our bodies from their original, near-perfect state.

Becoming and staying overweight and obese are directly connected to the early onset of many causes of preventable, premature death. Some of these are heart disease, stroke, Type 2 diabetes, and certain types of cancer.

Dr. Anne Case says, "People may want to soothe the beast. They may do that with alcohol, they may do that with drugs, they may do that with food."[35] Unfortunately, indulging in excessive food intake of the wrong kinds is how more and more Americans are seeking to numb the pain of life.

The number of daily calories required for body fuel depends upon our level of physical activity and rate of metabolism. The daily calories needed by moderately active adult men are estimated to be 2,600, and for women, 2,000. Individually, to maintain a healthy weight, you may need more or fewer calories than recommended.

The old saw, "Well, my metabolism has slowed down, so I can't help but gain weight," has been blown out of the water. A breakthrough study[36] concluded that metabolism differs for all people across four distinct stages of life.

- From infancy until age one calorie burning is at its peak, accelerating until it is 50 percent above the adult rate.
- Then, from age one to about age 20, metabolism gradually slows by about three percent a year.
- From ages 20 to 60, it holds steady.
- After age 60, it declines by about 0.7 percent a year.[37]

Gina Kolata wrote in *The New York Times*, "The metabolic slowing that starts around age 60 results in a 20 percent decline in the metabolic rate by age 95. Dr. Klein (Director of the Center for Human Nutrition at the Washington University School of Medicine in St. Louis) says that although people gain on average more than a pound and a half per year during adulthood, they can no longer attribute it to slowing metabolism. Once the researchers controlled for body size and the amount of muscle people have, they also found no differences between men and women."[38]

The results of this study were "new news" and took away another "I can't help it" justification for weight gain in middle-age and beyond. Another aging myth bites the dust!

As we get older, not only do our daily caloric requirements decrease, but the *balance* of needed nutrients typically changes. A sedentary male over the age of 70 requires around 2,000 calories. With more significant activity, up to 2,600 calories a day could be acceptable. A female older than 70 years should eat between 1,600 to 2,000 calories daily depending upon her activity level.[39]

There are certainly cases where obesity is not self-caused, and not everyone who carries extra weight develops health problems. Instead, multiple factors contribute to obesity, including genetic, dietary, economic, psychosocial, reproductive, and pharmacological ones.[40]

Researchers have concluded there is an urgent need to find more ways to address diet, exercise, and lifestyle factors that contribute to weight gain, including nutrition education, access to safe places to walk or exercise, and support for avoiding sedentary behavior.

One choice among many we make is *what* food to put into our bodies (not just how much we eat). Over the past four decades, the consumption of food away from home has substantially risen. Regularly eating out can lead to excess calorie intake due to large portion sizes and the make-up of the foods offered. Many "fast foods" fall into this category. They are often high in calories, fat (including saturated and trans fats), sugar, simple carbohydrates, and sodium (salt).[41]

In many places today, the calories attached to fast food choices are displayed where they are purchased. But most of us look past them as we place our orders. Some of the well-known fast food choices and their typical calories include:[42]

- McDonald's Double Quarter Pounder with Cheese: 780 calories. Add a large Coke (+290) and an order of fries (+510), and you're looking at a meal that will load you up with 1,600 calories.
- Chick-Fil-A's Sausage, Egg, and Cheese Biscuit: 670 calories. This breakfast item features 19 grams of saturated fat—95 percent of the recommended daily value.
- Arby's Triple Decker Club: 1,030 calories. Turkey, bacon, ham, roast beef, two types of cheese, lettuce, and

mayonnaise between two slices of honey wheat bread. Even the list of ingredients is mouthwatering, but perhaps not enough to spend half a day's recommended caloric intake.

- Sonic's Super Sonic Bacon Double Cheeseburger (with mayo, of course): 1,280 calories. The calories-from-fat on this one is a staggering 830.
- KFC's Chicken and Waffles Sandwich: 1,100 calories. If you want syrup, add 80 calories for each serving.
- Five Guy's style fries (just the fries): 953 calories. If you add a bacon cheeseburger (920 calories), the total comes to 1,873.
- You might say, "Well, I'm going to eat healthy today and just have a tuna sandwich." The Club Tuna on French bread (with mayo blended in) at Jimmy John's will deliver 1,050 calories.

There are socio-economic factors at work here too. Fast food is cheap, accessible, and, uh, *fast*. These elements can help strained budgets, working parents and reduce the need for transportation.

But fast food is only part of the "food chain" relating to the obesity epidemic. According to one journal:

> Yes, fast food and convenience foods are more prevalent today than ever before. And yes, portion sizes and caloric intake have increased. But that doesn't mean that these are the only culprits in our growing battle with the bulge. *The wholesale lack of physical activity is the*

> primary reason *for our expanding waistlines.*[43] [Emphasis added.]

Obesity is one of the great levelers of our time—rich or poor, we can all grow beyond our "ideal weight." At a quarter of a pound weight gain every other month (the weight of a single McDonald's Quarter Pounder patty before cooking) for ten years, your weight will be up by 30 pounds. The extra weight will have been accumulated at a rate of growth that is imperceptible to most.

What might carrying that extra weight feel like? Do this test (with your doctor's permission): Walk up a flight of stairs and then down. Now, pick up two grocery bags weighing 15 pounds (one for each arm), and walk up and down the stairs again. If you gain 30 pounds, your body will feel, all the time, as it did when you carried the bags.

Steve

I continue to marvel at your commitment to research and the graphics you find for our readers and me! You are a perfect role model for me stepping up my curiosity and seeking readily available answers as my numerical years advance.

The good news is that there is a mindful choice to be made in almost every case of obesity—an option to immediately begin reversing the approaches that have changed your wrapper into a health liability. Different choices about food intake and movement can have a profound impact on our quality of life. They directly affect how it *feels* to be alive *today* and every day.

We can all raise our awareness of the mindless, unhealthy

eating and drinking that lead to chronic disease and the potential for premature death. I am going to focus on just one element: healthier food choices. We can all learn about the foods, herbs and drinks that promote a better life.

There is a fundamental illusion that prevents us from committing to healthy eating. It is that unhealthy (often associated with "comfort") eating appears to be (and is) a readily accessible way to find pleasure and satisfaction while numbing our senses. As a result, we don't want to give up the joy we find in food and snacks that are delightfully tasty but have many unhealthful ingredients. "Not worth it! Not gonna do it! Too darn good!"

This illusion most noticeably kicks in after failed attempts at healthy eating. And those attempts are often driven by other people giving us unsolicited advice on the subject. So, the motivation to do it is flawed from the start. For motivation to "stick," it has to be ours, sincerely coming from within.

We may experimentally try to "eat healthily" and then feel like we are choking on a kale sandwich with sprouted grain bread chased down with a drink made of carrot juice and apple cider vinegar. So many of my tries at healthy eating went that way, and it wasn't long before I was back to "living in the moment" with much more delicious (or so my body thought) cheeseburgers and shakes. I'd tell myself, "My body knows what it wants. It wants a Whopper from Burger King. With cheese. And a large order of fries."

My problem was that I never took the time to look into how to approach a successful transition toward more healthful eating. I never gave my palate or my body a chance to learn to welcome the change. I wasn't willing to fully experience the fact that healthier foods are an acquired taste. If you gradually introduce a more nutritional diet, it will become as tastefully delightful as fast food ever was.

Not only that: giving it time to kick in and be acknowledged as tasteful allows you to start feeling other benefits that make it even more worthwhile. The positive effects on energy and mental clarity start showing up. After a while, when you go back to the food on the old standard menu, the headaches and bloat and fatigue (which used to be just a part of life) come back with a vengeance and quickly deliver an unmistakable message: Don't. Do. This. To yourself!

For me, choosing to move toward healthy eating had to be shifted from something "I really *should do*" to something I genuinely *want to do*.

All the choices we recommend in this book will lose their effectiveness if they live inside you as "I should." Take your time to determine the desirability—for you—of one choice over another. See if you really want it and are willing to be intentional. Ask yourself, "Will I commit to this? Am I willing to renew that commitment each day?"

My "I should" list always feels like a burden based on the judgment of others or my own chronic, esteem-lowering self-judgments. There's no juice in that battery. People don't respond well to being scolded. That's why I've always kept my "should do" list hidden away from the part of me that wants to feel good about life.

But things get done faster when I take the time to move a "should do" into a "want to" and give it the joyful energy contained in every genuine desire.

Mindful Choice #15

I commit to learning about, selecting, and eating food for more energetic, healthful, and disease-free living.

Conversation Sixteen
I'm Walkin', Yes Indeed

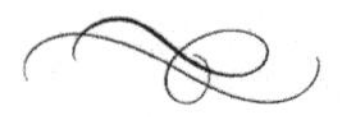

We offer our perspectives on and encouragement of greater mobility, conscious breathing, and mental acuity for more healthful years of living and greater happiness.

Steve

As I entered my mid-70s, I realized I had let myself get badly out of shape. We had just moved to Michigan from Arizona. By comparison, in Michigan, the winters were cold, and the sidewalks were sometimes slippery with ice. The excuses began to pile up. I even embraced the excuse we are advocating so strongly against accepting: "I'm getting too old." I turned it into a somewhat convincing argument: "Don't be foolish. Stay *safe*. At *your age*, you don't want to fall and break something."

When the COVID virus hit, lockdown provided me with another "valid" excuse to stay sedentary. Now I really *couldn't* go to the gym—it wasn't permitted! I wouldn't want to break the law in the interest of my physical conditioning!

But by then, I'd righted the ship mentally and knew I'd been using the crutch of "aging" as a good reason for all kinds of things I wasn't doing. I was actually avoiding them through a mere lack of creativity and, more importantly, from the absence of a consistent commitment to engage and practice. Not due to age.

As you referenced in our last conversation, "The wholesale lack of physical activity is the primary reason for our expanding waistlines."[44]

Eating better is essential but must be coupled with some physical activity. To overcome inertia, we have to take steps that work best for us.

Prison food is not widely recognized for its flavor and support of the inmates' optimal health. And, of course, prison cells aren't exactly built for walking. Not ideal conditions for staying healthy. Yet, I'd always known about and seen pictures of federal prison inmates who had improved their strength and fitness while incarcerated. Some became so powerful and fit that the wardens ordered the heavy barbells to be taken away from the prison exercise yard. It didn't stop the prisoners. They kept making their way to better health with pushups, pull-ups, and other always available bodyweight exercises in their cells.[45]

Why couldn't I innovate like that? So, rather than buy a huge treadmill that I could easily have fallen off given my sorry state of fitness and balance, I set up "walking circuits" for the basement, the downstairs, and the upstairs in my home. I wanted to have walking space on a floor where my wife Kathy wasn't. Not only did I not want to bump into her, but I was also worried that she'd be seeing me (someone who she already suspected was a little crazy) walking round and round in circles in front of her very eyes.

I'd always known that what gets measured gets done, so I also bought a pedometer and kept my daily steps recorded in a little notebook.

I'd been a huge advocate of walking in my younger years, but for creativity reasons, not for health. I'd read about how Ralph Waldo Emerson did his best writing after a long walk. I'd heard nutrition and wellness expert Dr. Andrew Weil explain how walking brought the right side of the brain (where creativity and imagination live) out and into active harmony with the left side. Because the right side of the brain activates the left side of the body and the left side activates the right side of the body, when we walk (left, right, left, right), the rhythm of the footfalls lights up the mind with whole-brain thinking and creative inspiration. It works!

The National Institutes of Health (NIH) is the primary agency of the U.S. government responsible for biomedical and public health research. The NIH is ranked number two in the world, behind Harvard University, for biomedical science research. And they have done extensive research on the benefits of walking. Most interesting to me was their recent study on the relative significance of the number of steps taken each day. I found it so interesting that I wrote the findings down in my pedometer notebook so I'd see it each time I recorded my steps.

A study of people over 40 found that "Adults who took 8,000 or more steps a day had a reduced risk of death over the following decade than those who only walked 4,000 steps a day. And, step intensity (number of steps per minute) didn't influence the risk of death, suggesting that *the total number of steps per day is more important than intensity*."[46]

In other words, you can walk fast or slow and still lower your risk of death. And when you read the research, you will see that the increased number of steps dramatically impacted how long you may stay alive *and* in good health.

I sometimes cue up the Bee Gees' infectious song "Stayin' Alive" or Tom Petty's "I'm Walkin'" when I walk. If you go back in years as far as I do, you could fire up the original version of "I'm Walkin'" by Fats Domino, which was a hit in the 50s and later covered successfully by Ricky Nelson. All the arrangements are fun to walk to.

So now that I've called myself out on exercise, it's your turn, Will, to tell us what you do at your "advanced age." I know it will probably be more extensive than this because you are a few years younger than I am (which, once again, likely means nothing or too little to matter). And I also recall that you were a successful college track and field athlete who once was in top shape.

Will

Firstly, Steve, I absolutely love that you are taking steps to improve your physical wellness by *taking steps*. As you point out, this alone can change your attitude, your brain function, basic fitness, and even the length (let alone quality) of your life expectancy. As we say in business, that is a very high return on investment.

My choices today are still shaped by the fact that I considered myself an "athlete" growing up. I earned a four-year athletic scholarship that paid for my college tuition and expenses. Five days a week, I would go to my "job" as a part of the track and field team and spend two to three hours at the practice facilities. I spent about half the time on fitness and weight training, and the other half on the skills required for the various events that were my focus. I loved it and had the good fortune to be successful.

Since then, I have been in and out of physical exercise of many kinds, depending upon the other demands in my life and, as with most other adults, the level of dedication I was able to muster at the time. A few years ago, I found myself sedentary and not paying much attention to what I was eating and drinking. Then, one day, I noticed that my energy was lagging, and I had gained some weight (and it wasn't muscle).

I was fortunate that my starting point for making a change wasn't being obese. Even with that advantage, I started the same place that you have suggested, Steve—walking. I started nice and easy. Like you, when I had phone calls (the old-fashioned kind without video), I walked a circuit in my apartment. I tracked my steps on an app on my phone. Often when I completed a call, I would see that I had walked over 2,000 steps! I have since made this a habit with each call I make or receive. When the phone rings, I immediately stand and start walking.

Just as with the other choices we've discussed, it is a matter of first raising your awareness of the opportunities around you to get into motion. Simple starting points are everywhere: Walking to the mailbox. Taking the long way into the mall by parking (safely) at the far end of a well-lit parking lot. Taking the stairs instead of an elevator or escalator. Regularly walking your dog (or the neighbor's). Getting moving before breakfast and after dinner. It adds up. Suddenly, you will discover you have greater mobility and flexibility. You will breathe some outside air and get more vitamin D from having the sun light you up a bit. You will see what is going on outside your four walls!

Over time, this process of walking daily—the good feelings,

weight loss, and clear head that came with it—led me to renew my interest in fitness training. So, last year I started doing fitness exercises a few days a week. After a while, and with some fits and starts due to a wide variety of excuses I offered myself, I found a trainer to work with me. I realized I needed the motivation of an "appointment" to get me up and out.

Over several months, my trainer helped me with weight training, balance, mobility, flexibility, and a "core" strengthening program.[47] In the process, I learned that most of the basic fitness exercises I was doing could be done at home using my body weight and without equipment.

As a result of sticking with this routine, I have gained strength, flexibility, improved balance, and more erect posture (my slumping was starting to make me look old and tired—as if)!

This activity has had a remarkable impact on every aspect of my life. Now, I don't want to miss out on my exercise. If I miss a session, I feel I have cheated myself out of a change of scene in my day and a boost for my body and psyche. I love how I feel, and I have more stamina for everything else.

You can start getting exercise in other ways. Even if you don't have a yard or room for a garden, many cities and towns now have community gardens. You can sign-up for a small plot and take care of plants, flowers, fruits, and vegetables, as though it was your place. The exercise benefits from gardening can be valuable (and you can get your hands in the dirt).

If someone you know has a yard that needs help, make the offer to assist. Maybe engage them in creating a new landscape plan and then work on it together. Exercise can add interest, connections, variety, and fun to your life, and ultimately a fitter body for the long haul.

Mindful Choice #16

I will integrate enjoyable, repeatable ways of getting my body in motion. I will track my progress and raise my awareness of the benefits of doing so.

Conversation Seventeen
"Will You Be Bullied by Fear?"

We reveal the truth about fear and offer a proven method to unmask it.

Will

"I couldn't try that, I'm too afraid." I've never done it before. It's too hard. What if I can't do it? I might get hurt. I would try it, but I don't have time. If somebody else did it with me, I might. If I did it, I might not be able to do the other thing. What would people say if I tried, and I wasn't able to? I'm too young to try it. I'm way past the age where that would be appropriate. I'm too old. If I did it, I might die."

It doesn't really matter what "it" is; these are statements and questions we have heard throughout our lives (often in the form of self-talk) and just a small sampling of reasons and excuses for not doing things due to a perception of fear. It could be fear of failure and exposure as a fallible human being (a truly terrible thing!), though fear of success in some form is just as likely.

The only one of these that might be a valid reason for avoidance is, "I might die." The rest are just negotiating the quality and depth of your life experiences with yourself.

There are very few decisions you will make in your lifetime, where one of the likely outcomes will be death. Yes, of course, you can play Russian roulette with a handgun, or attempt to walk across the 405 freeway in L.A. at rush hour, or (as a non-swimmer) jump into the ocean from a cruise ship. I would say these are not very well-disguised suicide options.

The phrase "I might die" is overused as an excuse for choosing not to do something. It is also a false statement because the only truthful one is, "I *will* die," as will all living beings. But the latter phrase is not germane to most of the things that we avoid doing.

Most of the time, this fear presents itself as a potential "symbolic death." It could be "I would die of embarrassment if my friends saw me looking like this," or, "I would just die if our neighbors knew we can't afford to keep our kids in private school anymore." The threat of death isn't present, except as an extreme overstatement of potential consequences.

"Nothing in life is to be feared. It is only to be understood."

~ Marie Curie

Steve, you and I both know a modern sage of a woman named Byron Katie. She created and developed something humbly known as "The Work." It is a beautifully simple yet powerful method for exposing the small and even complex lies we tell ourselves. We recommend reading any of her books, but as an introduction, suggest her book, *Loving What Is*.

Let's explore the expression "I might die" through the lens of a possible dialogue between Katie and one of her seminar attendees. The questions and answers might go something like this:

"So, you're telling me you might die if someone in your office found out that you have two children but have never been married?"

"Yes, absolutely. I could never show my face there again."

"Okay, you might have to quit for your own reasons, but you said you might die. Isn't that quite different from not being able to show your face there again?"

"No, it would be like dying for me—it would be so embarrassing."

"So, it would be embarrassing for you to the point where death would be a better alternative?"

"Well, the job means so much to me that I cannot imagine being able to stay if they found out."

"Let's stick with your first statement that you will die if someone finds out your secret. Is that really true? Would you die? You would stop breathing, and your heart would stop.? Is that true?"

"No, I probably wouldn't die, but it feels like that when I think about it."

"So, it's a feeling, not a fact. Is that true?"

"Yes, it's a feeling, but I can imagine it actually happening."

"So, it's a feeling, and you aren't really going to die?"

> "Well, no, but it would be uncomfortable, and I might have to explain my circumstances."
>
> "Can you imagine doing that? What would you say?"
>
> "I might say that I very much wanted to have children but had not been able to find a man who I thought would be the kind of father I would want for my children. I was in my early 40s and felt I was running out of time, so I decided to adopt two children on my own."
>
> "And you believe that if your co-workers discovered this truth that you would die?"
>
> "I guess not. I hadn't really thought it through like that. It doesn't sound so bad now that you've asked me the questions."

We so often infuse circumstances with a perceived power of life and death. And never question the assumptions we are making! You can see, Steve, what happened here when the statements were simply but directly challenged and honestly answered.

We avoid people and experiences and opportunities to sidestep the *possibility* of being embarrassed or suffering a little fear or stage fright. Yet, at any point, we can engage in cross-examinations of our fears and assumptions and take away the power they never deserved in the first place. We can do this whenever we might be fooling ourselves into avoiding life experiences.

We all find ways to limit and avoid experiences in many clever and self-sabotaging ways. I believe that perceived risk is put in its place by the truism, "The downside of risk is almost always overrated." If we think back on what was missed by being unwilling to get outside our comfort zones, it could be a pretty long list. In hindsight, the risks avoided were probably benign in most cases.

I haven't counted, but some say that the phrase "Do not be afraid," appears in the Bible over 350 times. Apparently, it is a hard lesson to remember, no matter who you are.

Maybe now that completing our time on Earth is closer than our arrival, we could take a little more risk. The only thing that likely will happen is proving that there is more to living than mere survival.

There is power in awareness of the constraint of time. Using it by taking on some new experiences might be a blessing.

Steve

Thank you, Will, for bringing up the work of Byron Katie. She is truly an enlightened sage for our time. Her book *Loving What Is* provides all of us, no matter what age, a simple tool for inquiry whereby any fearful thought can be dismantled and dissolved. Her books and videos (available for free online), and her Nine Day School for the Work, dramatically changed my life.

You raised such an important line of inquiry. I like to explore it from this angle: What would I do with my life *if I had no fear?*

That usually opens my mind to possibilities I hadn't allowed myself to look at before. So, I see clearly, as you say, ". . . there is more to living than mere survival."

If our life force, filled as it is with divine creativity, is only to be used to survive, then we live in a fear-based way, genuinely missing out on what's possible. And as you mentioned earlier, we *almost always* overestimate the downside of risk in potential acts of exploration, innovation, and courage.

Our culture's fear of death is at the heart of all of this. Some cultures celebrate a loved one's death with nights of dancing, singing, and drinking, so solid and sure is their belief (or knowledge?) that their loved one has ascended to a better place.

Contrast that with our more culturally embedded belief (or superstition?) that death is an awful voyage of bleak and lonely nothingness. This was captured most poignantly in Dylan Thomas's famous poem, "Do Not Go Gentle into that Good Night." It was about the imminent death of his elderly father. The poem ends this way:

> And you, my father, there on the sad height,
> Curse, bless, me now with your fierce tears, I pray.
> Do not go gentle into that good night.
> Rage, rage against the dying of the light.

The point here is that inquiry, sincerely practiced, will dissolve all the superstitions that fears are based on. It can be done alone, or with a skilled coach or spiritual teacher. It can be done at 19 or 99. I did this myself, and I had as fear-based an ego as could possibly be. After that turnaround, which occurred in my 50s, I was able to witness and even help facilitate that process with hundreds of clients worldwide. They could often see that if I could do it, anyone could.

Will

Some see the word fear as an acronym for "false evidence appearing real." Interrogation of the true facts and circumstances upon which any fear is based will almost always expose the lie that is at the center of it.

To conclude this conversation, I offer my two favorite quotations on fear and risk:

> "If you are distressed by anything external, the pain is not due to the thing itself, but to your estimate of it, and this you have the power to revoke at any moment."
>
> ~ Marcus Aurelius

And the other exposes the false belief that there is any place where we can be completely safe and secure:

> "Security is mostly a superstition. It does not exist in nature, nor do the children of men as a whole experience it. Avoiding danger is no safer in the long run than outright exposure. The fearful are caught as often as the bold."
>
> ~Helen Keller

Recognizing the existence of fear is the first step in moving past it. The second step is taking *any* action—no matter how small—that slaps it in the face. A good example is an unrelenting interrogation. As kids, with a greater willingness to try things (and less fear of risk), we might have said, "*I'm* not afraid!" and "*You* are not the boss of *me*!"

Take that, fear.

Mindful Choice #17

I will cross-examine my fears to explode the false assumptions that underlie them and reveal them for the life-sucking, experience-blockers they represent.

Conversation Eighteen
Setting Intention: A New, Old Law of Attraction

We consider the power of clearly setting intentions for what we choose to accomplish, daily renewal as the "secret sauce," and the value of simple, visible reminders.

Will

What if we could attract whatever we need or want, whenever we need or want it? Some might jump ahead and say, "I know what this is; they're going to feed us some quantum physics-based law of attraction 'faith-science.'" Or, "Thank goodness, finally some reality here! Everyone knows that engaging the law of attraction is *the* way to get what you want."

There is much tugging at each end of whether creating "attraction" is a matter-based, scientifically verifiable, repeatable process, an energetic personal belief system based upon continuous, vigorous affirmations, or something else.

The power of attraction is a belief that "thinking it can make it so," and in some quarters has attracted the label of pseudoscience. There have been some gurus, writers, speakers, and some charlatans, who have made good livings for years explaining the "law" of attraction. Imagine a four-hour seminar unpacking the three words: "Thoughts are things."

My belief, Steve, is that it is much simpler. It makes no claim to science, but I have discovered something that works to attract what I need. Moreover, it is something we have all successfully done, in most cases intermittently.

It is called intention setting.

If you set an intention for something you want or need to create, see, do, acquire, or even "be," you will soon find yourself covered with a pile of options to take you where you want to go. Since I began trusting this method, it has proven true for me.

Setting an intention allows you to distinguish what is relevant for accomplishing your objectives versus everything else in the relentless river of images, noise, and other bombardments that come at us all day, every day.

When you and I work on a book (separately or, in this case, together), we set an intention to discover material that may in any way relate to the book's subject matter. For example, suppose we plan to write about accomplished musicians who started singing or playing an instrument after 75. We will extract what is necessary from the avalanche of information flow: the facts, stories, anecdotes, photos, books, movies, overheard conversations, billboards, even cereal boxes and junk mail. We will see and hear the bits of information that might have a potential connection to what we intend to "attract." We will filter out the nonsense (and sense) that doesn't relate to the topic at hand.

It won't be long before we say, "I had no idea there was so much information about people who embraced music after they turned 75. It's everywhere!" If you tell others about your intention, you will multiply your inputs. They will not be able to help *themselves* from seeing things that are relevant to your story. You will have created an even larger net to catch what you need. You may even make a friend or inspire others after inviting some help.

I found the C.S. Lewis quotation at the front of this book painted on the fence of a home that backed up to a greenbelt where I sometimes walk. Here it is again: "You can't go back and change the beginning, but you can start where you are and change the ending."

If we weren't writing this book, I may or may not have seen it or read it. But because I had set an intention to discover anything that might enhance the content of this book, I identified it immediately as "potential resource material"! I took a photo of it with my smartphone, confirmed it was accurate, then suggested to you that we use it. A quote on a fence in Portland, Oregon, made it into the very beginning of this book. It was a direct consequence of setting an intention.

The clearer we can be in setting an intention, the greater energy we will generate in discovering what is needed. Try on some of the statements of intention that follow. But be forewarned. You will *not be able to ignore them* if you bring them to a conscious level.

I intend to:

- Recognize people in the acts of being kind to others.
- Find a part-time job I can do from home.
- Learn about mindfulness.
- Discover recipes for cooking quick meals for two.
- Meet people who could be walking companions.

- Join a book club for lovers of nonfiction.

Setting an intention is about becoming self-guided in sorting the wheat from the chaff relating to a particular task or interest. It has enormous applicability in everyday life. To learn about something, meet someone, or be part of a group interested in [fill in the blank], just set an intention, and magic will happen. And yes, the magic is in noticing—the same "noticing" we have mentioned many times in previous conversations.

Intention is the ultimate magnet: discovering the energetic connections that are all around us but which, in the absence of an intention, are almost invisible.

Steve

I have very little to add about the power of intention here, Will, because you've said it all. I know it will inspire many people. I also highly recommend Wayne Dyer's book, *The Power of Intention*. Reading it represented a major turning point in my life. Dyer says, "You get what you intend to create by being in harmony with the power of intention, which is responsible for all of creation."

Setting clear intentions gives life direction and clarity. And what's the alternative? Well, people can always allow the later years of their lives to be rudderless and confused, spun around by the myths of aging and being perpetually reminded that getting what you want is for the young and ambitious. "It's far too late to be intentional about something you want to do, and it's a waste of your time, Grandpa."

Although I don't accept remarks like that as having

applicability to *me*, I must confess that one of the problems I had in utilizing the power of intention was my forgetfulness. I'd set an intention, and then, over time, it would fade from my memory. I'd default to just reacting to whatever problem came up. I'd sometimes vaguely notice that I was responding all day and never creating anything. The intention I had set earlier would somehow disappear.

That's when it hit me that I needed a system to keep my intentions front-and-center. So, I started putting my current ones up on a whiteboard in my bedroom or office—anywhere I would see it first thing each day. This "intention visibility" can be done in many different ways—not just this one.

Recently, after a year of the pandemic lockdown at home, I noticed some ill effects mentally and physically from not being out in the world. So, I set an intention to get out more. But I knew that mentally noting it wouldn't be enough. So, I put a post-it note above my computer, which I see every morning. Just three words: "Get out more."

It worked like a charm. As days went on and I was at my computer wandering through my favorite sites, Kathy called out to me that she was going out to a garden center to look for some plants and flowers for the backyard. Ordinarily, I'd have just said, "Okay, have fun!" and returned to my screen. But because my intention to "get out more" was right up there in front of me on the note, I said, "Hang on, I'll go with you." And we'd have a great time enjoying the garden center and our time together out of the house. That's a small thing, I know. But I'm happier and healthier because of it, so maybe it's not really that small.

The point is a simple one for me: The power of intention is a *real* power. But an intention can't work its magic if it's forgotten. So, keeping it front and center is something I must do to make sure I take full advantage of this power.

Mindful Choice #18

I will add the power of intention setting and commitment to my arsenal of tools for developing a richer, happier life and create what I need to make it happen, starting now.

Conversation Nineteen
Refuse to be Ushered Offstage

Steve reflects on the rewards of singing and not falling for the "I'm too old" myth. We discuss the importance of self-expression and avoiding censorship—your own and especially that pushed your way by others.

Steve

There are remarkable studies on the positive effects of music on the brain. Some conclude that mood and cognitive function improve simply through regularly listening to music. And music has recently been shown to be of enormous value in memory-care facilities—in some cases reawakening memory in the brains of patients with everything from mild dementia to advanced Alzheimer's.

For the moment, I want to focus on a particular aspect of music: singing. Singing, especially in my 60s and 70s, has dramatically elevated the quality of my life and improved my happiness.

I began singing in my teens in the 1950s and the 1960s. I was shy and tongue-tied around teenage girls. I longed for romantic relationships, but they were not happening. This was right around the time that Elvis Presley came upon the scene and began to appear on television. He seemed shy and tongue-tied, too. That is, right up until he started singing and beaming his beautiful smile at all the girls in the audience, who were cheering and screaming for him and his musical performance.

I decided to take a page from Elvis, and why not? I bought a guitar and learned to play and improved my singing.

I wasn't exceptionally talented as a singer, but I was good enough and very willing to learn and practice. So, I learned to play and sing my favorite songs, some of them from Elvis, Ricky Nelson, Ray Charles, and some of the standards by Frank Sinatra, Nat King Cole, and others.

It wasn't long before people started asking me to bring my guitar to parties and other gatherings. I entered a talent show in junior high and did some singing performances in high school. But, even after my original intention of getting to know and be more appealing to girls came to be, my singing became more than that. I began singing and songwriting with friends and later performing here and there in bars and gyms and at weddings and receptions.

But then I grew up and entered the real world. I had a career and a family, and I set my guitar aside. It got dusty, strings broke, and it began to look like a deteriorating symbol of a lost and joyful period of youth. But in my 60s, my wife's parents gave us a beautiful (and very large) Steinway piano they couldn't fit into their new house. Every time I walked past it, it called to me. So, I began sitting down to it more and more, learning how to play it. It rang out with great volume, and I had to strengthen my voice and lung power as I went along, to sing with it.

That's when the true joy of singing returned to my life.

Almost by accident. The unexpected gift of a piano! The effects on my physical well-being and enjoyment of life were profound. I kept improving my singing abilities, and the positive results continued.

"If I were not a physicist, I would probably be a musician. I often think in music. I live my daydreams in music. I see my life in terms of music. I get most joy in life out of music."

~Albert Einstein

I did notice some of *those* thoughts, though. The ones we've been talking about: Am I too old for this? Won't my voice get weak and frail with age? Am I even being "age-appropriate" by singing and wailing on the piano and guitar like this? What will the neighbors think?

I even started taking voice lessons in my 70s. I asked my teacher if the reason I wasn't hitting some of the notes I was able to do when I was younger was a simple matter of age. He said, "No, it's a simple matter of proper practice."

I told him I remembered my grandmother at my age singing with a creaky, wavering voice. An old person's voice. You can hear how old people are when they sing or even speak, right?

"Wrong," my voice coach said. "You are hearing that they haven't been singing or speaking or even breathing as much as they used to. That's what you're hearing. Not age."

So, we pressed on with my lessons, and it turned out he was right. After enough regular rehearsal and practice, I had more vocal range at the age of 74 than at 24. So now it was getting fun and exciting.

The great philosopher and psychologist William James once said, "I don't sing because I'm happy; I'm happy because I sing."

He said in one sentence what I've tried to say here in many paragraphs!

In an article in Healthline magazine, it was noted, "People love to sing. Whether or not they can carry a tune, people seem to understand that there's something positive—something healthy—in the act of raising their voices in song. In fact, there's solid scientific evidence to prove that singing is good for your body and your mind. Decades of research have shown that singing individually and in groups is good for you on many levels."[48] And then they list some of them:

- Relieves stress
- Stimulates the immune response
- Increases pain threshold
- May improve snoring
- Improves lung function
- Develops a sense of belonging and connection
- Enhances memory in people with dementia
- Helps with grief
- Improves mental health and mood
- Helps improve speaking abilities

So, now, knowing about that research, what would stop anyone from singing? Singing in the car and in the shower? Or hearing their favorite songs and singing along? Or joining a singing group in town? Or just walking through the house singing?

I'm guessing two things. Two beliefs: One, you might say, "I'm not a good singer." And two, "I'm too old for singing."

These thoughts, familiar as they are, have no value or relevance. I wasn't a good singer either at the start, but I got better. Anyone can get better, and the progress of getting there is really gratifying. And all the benefits of singing will accrue no matter how "good" a singer you think you are.

The second thought is related to what everything in this book is arguing against: "I'm too old."

Here's a thought from Ashton Applewhite, the author of *This Chair Rocks: A Manifesto Against Ageism*. "We are aging differently and in more healthy ways than our parents, and certainly our grandparents. We are refusing to be ushered offstage gracefully. We want to continue to be in the world, to have purpose and to contribute."

You are not too old to sing. You just think you are. Get back on stage.

Will

When does the shutting down process begin in most of our lives? I believe it is so early in our development that most of us can't remember the first "shoooooosh," or "be careful," or "you're too little for that," or "you're too big for the other thing," or "you might hurt yourself." These comments are made by well-intended parents, based upon learned approaches from *their* parents, and so on, back into the dark ages of caution. (I am, of course, *not* referring to the need to stop a toddler about to put her hand in the deep fryer.)

The discouragement continues, at an increasing pace: "She's not smart [or pretty, or good] enough to be with *our* group," "Don't pick him for our team, he's too small [or large]," or "He doesn't even have his own ball glove." The latter was the reason I never played baseball, not even recreationally—ever. I never got over the initial embarrassment of my mom not being able to afford one and was too ashamed to borrow one, so I let the game go. It sounds ridiculous today, but if I remember it 60 years later, it must have made an indelible impression.

In going down this kind of memory lane, we all will think of things that might have become passions. But we were shut down and didn't realize, or hadn't been taught, that small minds are a plague, and are everywhere.

Before I went to high school, I played basketball and was on the football and track teams. I also played the oboe and tenor and baritone saxophones. One year, I was named to the San Diego metro area honor orchestra for my age group.

As high school approached, I met with a guidance counselor about my classes and activities. He said, "High school is very different. You can't be in the band and play sports too. You won't be able to handle both. So, which do you choose?" I sat there taking this in and certainly didn't want to fail at anything—not in high school! So, I said, "Well since I can't do both, I am going to play sports." This set the table for the rest of my adult life to date, during which I never again picked up a musical instrument.

We can all recall examples of what we have given up by

accepting someone clipping our wings along the way. As older folks, we face a lot of the same cautions that children do: "Don't get up, I'll get you a cup of coffee, so you don't have to stand up—you know, your hip." Whaaaat? Or "You shouldn't walk out on the porch; you might fall down the steps!" Huuuuh? Or "You are too old to sing or dance. You look foolish gyrating around at your age!" Really?

Some are fortunate to have parents and others in their lives that offer encouragement or at least know when to stay out of the way. My daughter recently sent me a video she took of my grandson. Though he couldn't yet speak, he had awakened from sleeping and was unmistakably singing something that made him *feel good*. To her credit, my daughter didn't disturb him until he was finished. Nobody said, "Stop it," or "It's time for breakfast." They let him do his thing. It was not only a serene moment for his parents, but he wasn't shut down from creating something from his being. He will continue to be open to singing, maybe for the rest of his life.

This is a key for all older adults (and all parents, partners, husbands, wives, bosses, leaders of all types, and so on): Become aware that an unthinking, unnecessary, unthoughtful, mindless, tossed-off comment can have lasting consequences. These comments can be even more damaging in parent-child and boss-employee situations. The relative power positions assure that these kinds of messages may never be forgotten.

No other human can be permitted to shut our spirits down. If someone attempts to do so, it is in our power to reject it. We needn't say a word—except to ourselves, "I will make my own decision about that issue." On the other side of the ledger, we can be helpful to those around us. Think of serving them from the activist side of the human operating system choices we discussed earlier: owner, creator, optimist—and we could add "encourager."

Steve

I may be overdoing it, as I sometimes do with the things I love, but here is another story that illustrates the power of singing as an outlet for personal expression *and* service to others.

When the COVID pandemic arrived in America, there was early confusion about avoiding contracting it and passing it along. At the time, most of the advice I was seeing and hearing was to wash your hands, use sanitizer, wipe down grocery bags and food containers, and so on.

The disease experts learned pretty quickly that the virus was primarily passed along in the form of aerosols—particles in the air breathed, coughed, or sneezed out by infected people. Another person breathing in these aerosols could become infected with the virus.

A day or two before the national news carried the change in guidelines to include masks and social distancing, a friend of mine, Coizie Bettinger, washed her hands, put hand sanitizer in her purse, and went to a rehearsal of her beloved Skagit Valley Chorale. At the time, she was in her 70s and had been singing with the choir (they call it a Chorale) in rural Washington state for over 20 years.

No one going to that rehearsal, including Coizie, knew that a change in CDC guidelines had dramatically shifted ideas about gatherings of groups of people: that these could be COVID super-spreader events. They weren't aware at the time that gatherings, including singing groups, would be canceled everywhere later that same week.

She sang that day with the choir group without knowing the death and disease that would soon sweep through their members. Or that it would make national news. Much of the reaction to their gathering to sing was negative and accusatory—as though they had intentionally disregarded the recommendations. *The Los Angeles Times* story headline read, "A choir decided to go ahead with rehearsal. Now dozens of members have COVID-19, and two are dead."

When I heard the incident portrayed as clueless and reckless, it didn't match what I knew of Coizie. She was an artist whose gorgeous pastel paintings hang in our home. The last time I had been in her home in La Conner, Washington, she and I talked about our mutual love of music and singing, and she later sent me a CD of the Chorale's songs. They were marvelous.

On the website that presents her paintings, she wrote, "It is important to have things in our lives to remind us of our world's beauty and peacefulness. I want people to live with paintings of joy, hope, and harmony."

Those aren't the words of a negligent super-spreader of a deadly disease. They are the words of an inspirational, talented lady, always at the top of her game.

Fortunately for her reputation and those of her talented colleagues, *The New York Times* came out with the rest of the story a few months later. It was written with grace by Kim Tingley.[49] *The Times* story clarified that the Chorale members singing together that day did not know how dangerous those gatherings had become.

It went on to reveal the indomitable spirit and innovation of the Chorale by continuing to sing over Zoom during the lockdown.[50] We usually associate the energy for online innovation with young people (try editing together each singer's part from Zoom recordings, all of which come through at slightly different rates). But the Chorale was mostly made up of older folks, like Coizie.

They didn't have to continue on. They had taken a very public beating and could have just wilted away until they could safely gather and sing together again. The fact that they didn't fade out said something about who they were choosing to be. Coizie said, "It's a message about resilience and optimism and looking forward. We want to show the world that we've found a way to continue singing."

There's a larger message there for me as well—to have the rest of my life be as great as it can be, I, too, want to find a way to continue doing what I love, despite whatever circumstance threatens to lock me down.

Mindful Choice #19

Choose to express the music that lives inside you and let loose with other creative expressions that you were once blocked from or encouraged to give up—and did, until now.

Conversation Twenty
An Old Dog *Can* Learn

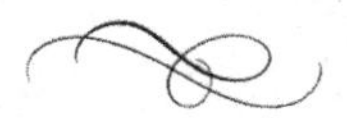

We celebrate neuroplasticity and share other discoveries about the human brain. We grind into dust variations on the saying, "You can't teach old dogs, new tricks."

Will

Earlier, we referred to neuroplasticity, a word with a definition not easy to guess (especially with "plastic" as a part of it). Simply put, neuroplasticity is our brain's ability to reorganize itself to serve us better. In certain circumstances, our brains can actively create new neural connections or improve existing ones. These are the pathways that support our sensory, motor, and cognitive skills and that ultimately regulate all our behavior. This rewiring capability does not stop with age, though the process will take longer as one gets older.[51]

The brain we bring into the world at birth is the basic model. It is a new computing system that is extremely busy during the first year of life. Our individual brains, of course, are not the same as everyone else's in terms of intelligence and potential future performance. However, all can be immediately harnessed for coping with the enormous world outside the comfort and complete environment of the womb.

If you watch a child during the first year of life, the rapid development of brain function is undeniably clear. It's as though you are watching a tiny human reading voraciously from an operating manual: locating body parts, learning to eat and drink, navigating (forward, back, and sideways) while crawling and standing upright, making different kinds of noises, and interacting with other humans, both parental and peer-sized.

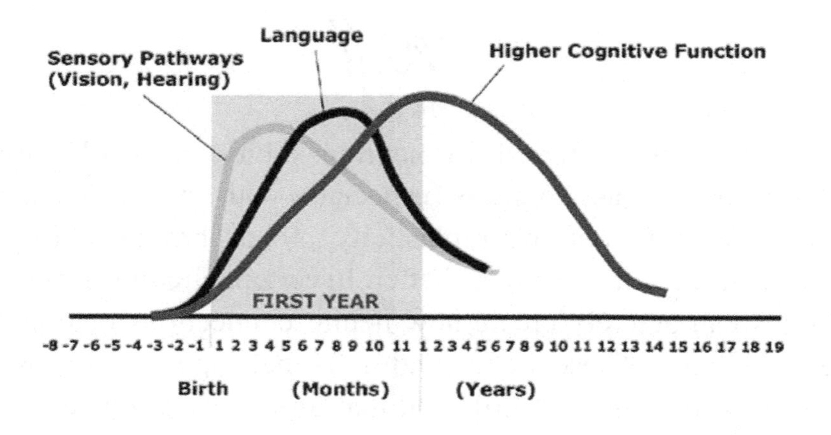

Basic training for brain management occurs very rapidly in that first year. A solid platform is created for education and experience to build up to "higher cognitive functioning" from there. Though the growth curves slow after the first year, experiential and other learning add pathways and adapt existing ones throughout life. Shelli R. Kesler, a senior research scientist at the Stanford University School of Medicine, says, "Neuroplasticity never ends, you can, in fact, teach an old dog, new tricks, it just might take a little longer."[52, 53]

The conventional wisdom has been that new brain pathways can be created in about three weeks. This was likely first outlined in the book *Psycho-Cybernetics* by Dr. Maxwell Maltz, initially published in 1960. However, current research suggests that new *automaticity* (the ability for new "tricks" to become habitual) varies between 18 and 254 days.[54]

Here's more about neuroplasticity:

> . . . neural connections can be forged and refined or weakened and severed. Changes in the physical brain manifest as changes in our abilities. For example, each time we learn a new dance step, it reflects a change in our physical brains: new "wires" (neural pathways) that give instructions to our bodies on how to perform the step. Each time we forget someone's name, it also reflects brain change, the "wires" that once connected to the memory have been degraded, or even severed. As these examples show, changes in the brain can result in improved skills (a new dance step) or a weakening of skills (a forgotten name).[55]

There are two main reasons our brains can make these shifts. The first is *structural* neuroplasticity, the ability of the brain to change its physical structure through repetition and learning. Think of learning something new: riding a bicycle, driving a car, learning a new language or musical instrument, completing a crossword or jigsaw puzzle. Education, repetition, and continuous learning will change brain functioning.

The second is *functional* neuroplasticity, including the ability of the brain to rewire itself in the event of structural damage. The brain can relocate functions from an injured or damaged area to one with healthy functioning equipped to handle them.

Our brains help us in other ways throughout our lifespans. For example, *brain agility* involves reframing a current approach to situations (e.g., from reacting to creating) and further developing currently underutilized brain functions.[56] (More information can be accessed through the footnoted sources.)

Another way is *mindset management*. For most things in life, we have a *fixed* mindset (what we know) instead of a *growth* mindset (an openness to creating something new.) Our conversations have emphasized the higher utility and more stimulating life benefits of being growth-minded rather than resting in the status quo.

> Most successful people tend to have a growth mindset and an ongoing desire to learn and develop personally throughout their life. As we get older, it can seem harder and more fruitless to try new things we believe we will not be successful at; however, by becoming aware of our resistance to change, it is possible to train ourselves to overcome this resistance and expose ourselves to new activities.[57]

Another idea to encourage our brains to continue serving us in new ways is to adopt a lifestyle of greater *simplicity* and *mindfulness*.

> Pressing the pause button on our hectic daily lives and helping simplify our brain's work can have a surprising impact on its ability to grow and change. Focusing all

our attention on the present moment, and our own breathing in the act of mindfulness, can have both long- and short-term physical benefits on the brain. Short term it will decrease our stress by reducing our levels of the stress hormone cortisol in the blood.[58]

Finally, another word about exercise. Yes, it helps brain function too. The brain is capable of neurogenesis [the process by which new neurons (nervous system cells) are formed in the brain] . . . and exercise stimulates this growth. In a way, exercise signals cells to start acting like stem cells, capable of new growth. In addition, exercise increases the brain's "baseline activity" which also stimulates cellular growth.[59] [Emphasis added.]

I hope this explanation helps make sense of a complex topic. The simple fact is that new experiences, exercise, curiosity, learning, and mindfulness fire up our mental capabilities and help maintain intellectual acuity.

We old dogs really can learn new tricks, and the process happens to be good for us.

Steve

I have very little to add to this, Will. But I will refer to it often now that you've spelled it out so concisely.

The innocent but absolute lie that says you can't teach an old dog new tricks, as we've pointed out, isn't true for humans *or* dogs. It is an excuse for staying with what is habitual and therefore comfortable (and encouraging others to do it, too). "I wouldn't bother trying to get Grandma to go to Zumba class.

You can't teach even nice old dogs new tricks!"

But one potential obstacle for older people learning new tricks is that, for some reason, we believe it should be *harder* than it may have once been. For example, I thought learning to play the piano was hard *because I was old.* I'd played guitar for years, but piano? Extremely hard, at my now "advanced age."

But I'd made a fundamental mistake. Unfortunately, I'd made the same wrong assumption when I took up weight training after decades of not doing it.

Yes, it was hard—but not because of my age (although that's a minor factor). Instead, the atrophy that came from lack of use was what made bringing muscles back, and re-learning an instrument, hard.

I was on the verge of missing out on the thrill of utilizing my brain's (now proven) plasticity. I'd thought my learning and strengthening years were over. Why? Because trying to get it back was hard. I had to finally wake up to the revelation (for me) that "hard" is not a signal to stop. "Hard" is not a negative or bad thing at all.

I recently watched a documentary about Apollo 11 and Neil Armstrong. Watching him walking on the moon called up for me the speech given by President John F. Kennedy years before the launch:

> We choose to go to the Moon in this decade and do the other things, *not because they are easy, but because they are hard.* Because that goal will serve to organize and measure the best of our energies and skills, because that challenge is one that we are willing to accept, one

> we are unwilling to postpone, and one which we intend to win, and the others, too. [Emphasis added.]

What is actually "harder" on seniors is staying on the sidelines due to the mythology that wants us to believe that we can't jump into the parade but should be content just watching it go by.

Will

Do you remember the radio DJs (or at least that's what they once were called) breathlessly shouting, "Stay tuned—the hits just keep on coming!" It's about time to say, "Stay tuned—the myths surrounding aging just keep on going." You recently sent me a link to a study you came across. I dug into it and wanted to share it.

It was a study of hundreds of older people conducted by Georgetown University Medical Center.[60] It confirmed that two key brain functions, which allow us to attend to new information and focus on what's important in a given situation can improve in older individuals. These two functions underlie memory, decision-making, and self-control.

> "People have widely assumed that attention and executive functions decline with age . . . But the results from our large study indicate that critical elements of these abilities actually improve during aging . . ." says the study's senior investigator, Michael T. Ullman, Ph.D., a professor in the Department of Neuroscience and director of Georgetown's Brain and Language Lab.

> The components studied are the brain networks involved in alerting, orienting and executive inhibition. [When you are driving a car, alerting is your increased preparedness when you approach an intersection. Orienting occurs when you shift your attention to an unexpected movement, such as a pedestrian. And executive function allows you to inhibit distractions such as birds or billboards so you can stay focused on driving.] The study found that both orienting and executive inhibition improved with age. The researchers hypothesize that because orienting and inhibition are simply skills that allow people to attend to objects selectively, these skills can improve with lifelong practice. The gains from this practice can be large enough to outweigh the underlying neural declines. Alerting declines because this basic state of vigilance and preparedness cannot improve with practice.

I'm beginning to believe that aging into "senior hood" may be much better than even *we* thought. Another myth bites the dust!

"And another myth gone and another one gone / Another myth bites the dust / Hey I'm gonna get yours too…"[61]

Mindful Choice #20

I will leverage my brain power in support of trying and doing new things and never offer the "Too old to learn or do" or "It's too hard" excuses.

Conversation Twenty-One
The (Not So Secret) Secret to Financial Sufficiency

We establish that many American families are financially fragile and explore the value of choosing to live within (or below) your means sooner rather than later.

Will

Choosing to live within or below our means, whatever they may be, is a vital choice. You will recall, Steve, that I dedicated about a third of my book *Untethered Aging* to this subject and believe it is essential to our discussion here too.

The challenges faced by U.S. households in making expenses match income are so pervasive that financial fragility has become a way of life. Income insufficiency is the rule for many. When asked to offer their view of Americans' financial situation, 95 percent of adults perceive that most Americans do not live comfortably.[62]

The challenges for senior Americans mirror those of other adults, with several important distinctions. As a percentage of the total working population, there are fewer employed older citizens. As a result, most are living on relatively fixed and lower incomes than when they were working. In addition, affordability issues are more challenging due to higher healthcare expenses and other aging-related costs. Complicating this is that longer life expectancies require paying for essentials for many more years.

The future for Social Security, a principal income source for many, is often debated by Congress as something for downward adjustment or overhaul, creating even more income uncertainty. Even the debate can cause anxiety among those dependent upon that income.

As mentioned in Conversation Six, Northwestern Mutual asked the following survey question: "What do you fear the most: Outliving your money in retirement or death?" Sixty-one percent said they were less afraid of dying. However, among those in their late 40s, married with dependents, the number fearful of outliving their assets rose to 82 percent.

Most seniors adapt to their post-employment financial situations. They make their way with Social Security and other non-work, non-savings, income sources. For the most part, they adjust their living expenses downward, even if they resisted doing so for most of their lives.

As we have established, forces beyond our control can take everything we possess except the freedom to choose how we respond. It becomes easier to develop actionable solutions if we can extract most of the emotion from our view of any problem. A problem is not inherently "bad," "good," or "embarrassing," and living is not the absence of challenges; it is overcoming them. This is true in the case of affordability issues.

I believe there are silver linings in an understanding of the facts about widespread financial insufficiency. There is a legitimate opportunity to hit the reset button on one of our most significant psychological stressors. There doesn't seem to be a path to do it collectively or at a governmental level, but we can do it individually.

One path to creating financial freedom (or getting as close as realistically possible) is to take available actions to ensure your expenses do not exceed your income. If you haven't taken these steps before now, it is most assuredly not too late. And now is a far sight better than later.

The resulting lifestyle may be different than the one you expected, hoped for, become accustomed to or even feel entitled to. It could be better than you thought, or you may find you feel regret for not having done more to prepare.

Wishing for the facts to move in your favor if you "give it time" is false hope. Honesty must be the foundation for recasting your financial situation to deal with fewer resources and a longer lifespan. Nobody else can call you out if you are uncommitted or denying reality. Nobody but you will have to live with the consequences.

There is a new attitude appearing in our culture that celebrates time and happiness over money. Today, some Millennials and other younger generations are saying, "I just want to make enough to cover the basics so I can live my life and do what I want to do. I just want to be happy." From where we sit, this seems a little naïve, but is also a refreshing point of view: not automatically accepting that working to "get ahead" is the only option.

Let's turn that around for older adults: Those who have transcended into senior status already have more time to explore life and happiness. They have more flexibility to live life as they want to and pursue happiness with greater commitment.

Sooner or later, a core question for every adult is this: "Is "having" more important than "being"? *Having* is the sufficiency of necessities and material possessions. *Being* is about personal development, individual expression, life experiences, and associations with others; it is the core premise of the mindful well-being choices we are offering here.

We believe you can both "have" and "be." Intentional choices for improved being (such as those suggested by us), when coupled with commitment, can elevate the quality and happiness of your living.

Less having could (and very likely will) lead to a greater sense of being. If you choose to live within your means and set an intention to do so, you will be amazed at the number of options available to reduce your spending.

Steve

Like so many people (and I thought I was alone in this until I started taking on coaching clients), I grew up with an abundance of money fears and issues. I was totally dysfunctional when it came to managing and saving money.

My father was successful in business but gone from home most of the time, and my mother was "gone" in her own way (on sedatives and alcohol). So, there was no one to learn from about life or money or responsibility. I became wild and free without a clue how to grow up—and without a desire to do so. I saw no point. Eventually, like my parents, I became a dedicated alcoholic. Money meant nothing. When I got it, I spent it. I was a "rebel" against society, and my life descended into my version of personal anarchy with no apparent exit.

But, as you say, Will, that approach won't work, and it didn't work for me. Free spending and willful ignorance about financial well-being create more misery than the "freedom" you think you're living. There is nothing "freeing" about it.

I was very fortunate to get clean and sober from alcohol and drugs in time to save my physical life. But the money problems remained. So, I had to go through a similar detox process from willful ignorance and irresponsibility in that arena. I had to ask for help.

I asked my accountant to relate to me as if I were a cognitively-impaired, underdeveloped child. He burst out laughing, thinking I was kidding. He'd liked some of the books I'd written and assumed I was a strong grown-up who had his act together. *Not when it came to money*, I assured him. It was a disaster.

I asked my life coach to help me release the immature, financially reckless personality I had thought was permanent. He gave me hope and many ways to reinvent who I was *being* around money and a lot of other issues

I asked my dear wife, who was and is (remarkably, in my eyes) extremely mature and grounded when it comes to money, to handle all our finances. She actually enjoys that kind of thing and promptly agreed.

Then I asked myself to be willing to accept—and eventually appreciate—living within my means.

To me, the big choice was between remaining in my willful ignorance about how to deal with money wisely or choosing to reach for a higher level of consciousness around it.

Earlier in my life, my then-psychologist, the well-known

Nathaniel Branden, had pointed out that my willful ignorance around money was dangerously self-destructive. He once said to me, "You're like a man who fears walking across a six-lane freeway so much that he puts on a blindfold before crossing so he won't see all those speeding cars and trucks in his way."

For an older person with diminishing sources of income and less time to improve their financial status, remaining blindfolded can be a real tragedy.

Your words above, Will, as they do in so many places in these conversations, have the potential to wake us up to what Dr. Branden kept telling me was the only solution to this: raising consciousness.

He would say, "Give me six quick answers to this sentence stem: 'If I brought five percent more consciousness to the way I'm handling money . . .'" and I'd list six things I'd naturally do differently and more effectively if I could bring higher consciousness to the issue.

The reason he always used "five percent more" in money (and all the other issues he helped me with) was that he knew human nature. We humans usually only think in polarities: "I'm either going to be good or bad at this. It's got to be 100 percent or nothing." He also knew that all real progress happens incrementally, in between the polarities, making progress and doing the doable until we get to where we want to be.

I'm living proof that one can learn anything late in life. The fears I had about dealing with reality were almost always unfounded and irrational, especially in the arena of money. Once I knew what my means were, living within them brought me freedom from the fear of not having what I need and can afford.

Taking the blindfold off and clearly understanding your financial situation (including its limitations) can be enormously freeing.

Mindful Choice #21

Starting right now I choose to make the necessary adjustments to my lifestyle to live within or below my means.

Conversation Twenty-Two
The Answers to Everything

We make the case that every adult and school-age child should have Internet access and learn the basics of navigating the vast amount of available knowledge and information. This access and capability are imperative for older adults in support of their independence and well-being.

Will

I know that "The Answers to Everything" is a bold title for this conversation, Steve, but I will prove it is not an exaggeration.

In my career as a business executive, I worked in the world of software and digital technology from the early days. Therefore, I had a bird's-eye view of the developments and innovations that changed how we communicate, learn, interact, do business, shop, travel, and many other aspects of living.

The creation of the Internet was a landmark breakthrough in digital technology history. Its architectural system, the World Wide Web (the "Web"), was made available to the public just 30 years ago! Since then, this technology platform has been chief among the enablers of global knowledge expansion.

Perhaps even more critical was the creation of the Web's organizing structure through the development of search engine platforms. This technology enables the knowledge on the websites and information repositories of the Web to be accessible from a screen on your desktop, tablet, smartphone, or other devices. Google is the best known of these platforms and today has about 92.5 percent of the global market share.[63] Google may not be the answer to everything, but it is without a doubt the principal global *gateway* to the answers to everything.

"Digital technology" suggests something intimidating and perhaps beyond the reach of people who grew up using paper, pencils, blackboards, erasers, and fingers and toes for counting (as we did). But no part of the population can ignore this incredibly easy-to-use tool and knowledge platform. So, I will show you below how you can learn to Google in less than five minutes.

It is possible and, I say, absolutely necessary, for every person of every age to be able to navigate the unlimited resources available through an Internet connection. There is no more critical knowledge access tool than Google for seniors.

Google is a direct and instantaneous way to access information and knowledge, from word definitions to travel videos to "Where is a 24-hour pharmacy near me?" or "Where is the closest emergency room?" By merely entering or asking a simple question, you will immediately be delivered answers. In most cases, lots of them. For example, try, "Okay, Google, what is normal aging?" If you make this inquiry, you will receive about 447 million reference points in half a second. Most people find what they need among the first few pages of the search results, typically the most relevant.

You might be surprised to learn that 25 percent of Americans 65 and older (13,500,000 people) do not use the Internet.[64] Yet, the efficiency of enabling people to get answers for themselves online versus making phone calls, driving, asking others, or paying third parties is well worth the modest investment of money and time to equip our citizens with this utility.

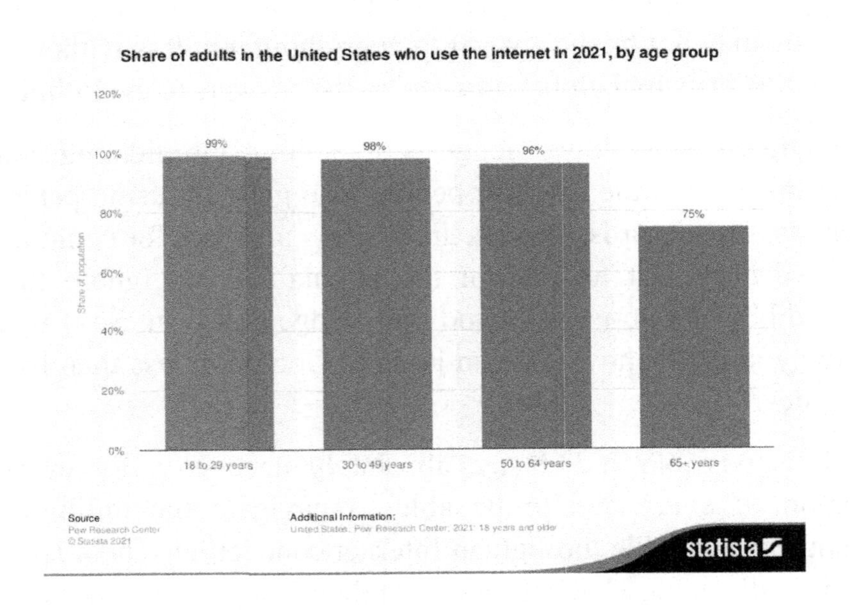

Even if you are among those without Internet access (or are not accessing it if you do have it), you will nonetheless recognize the brand names of some of the products that changed the world in just the *first ten years* of the 21st century. Their products and technologies have become integrated into our daily lives: iPod (2001), Wikipedia (2001), Skype (2003), Facebook (2004), YouTube (2005), Twitter (2006), Nintendo Wii (2006), the iPhone (2007), Amazon Kindle (2007), and the iPad (2010).

We have also seen the introduction and refinement of Bluetooth, GPS, the cloud, file sharing, hybrid cars, human genome sequencing, online streaming, the birth control patch, 3D printing, multi-use rockets, self-driving cars, the robotic heart, and much, much more.

Did I mention that you can also access virtually all library collections and travel the world through videos found on YouTube and other sites?

To have access to these and many other tools for living and entertainment, including video connections to your friends, children, grandchildren, and even medical care, you must have an Internet connection. If you don't, you can discuss how to get one with your family, neighbors, community centers, churches, and other local organizations. Among the seniors around you with smartphones (32 million), most will be happy to educate you and send you in the right direction for a solution.

How to Google in Three Steps[65]

Step One:

Once you have an Internet connection, go directly to Google.com by typing http://google.com into your web browser, a space found at the top of your screen. That will take you to the main Google website.

Step Two:

Type a question or describe in a few words what you're interested in finding into the search box on the Google website or your toolbar.[66] For example, "What is the capital of Missouri?"

Step Three:

Press the ENTER or SEARCH button and wait for the results of your search to appear on your screen. Depending upon the speed of your connection, you will usually get results to review in less than a second.[67]

You will have just Googled something!

The pace of change in our world will accelerate enormously over the next twenty years. To have the best life possible as an older adult, get this remarkable window on the world for yourself and open it. Using Google (or your choice of another search engine) will immediately change your life for the better.

Steve

There are severe consequences that come from not keeping up with how people communicate today. For example, many of the medically vulnerable seniors here in Michigan (and everywhere else) couldn't immediately get information and vaccinations needed during the COVID pandemic because they could not get online where the required information was first available.

And that's just one dramatic example. But it's a type of willful ignorance as challenging to one's health and physical well-being as the people in the old days who refused to get that crazy newfangled device called a telephone installed. If they lived in a rural area and needed a doctor quickly, they were out of luck unless their neighbor or family member could get to town fast enough on horseback or with a buggy.

That's one of the downsides of not keeping pace with advances in communication. I'm with you on the positive value and advantages of doing this, no matter how uncomfortable your mind tells you it will be to learn.

The upside of learning to keep up with new ways to communicate, even if you must swallow your pride and ask a younger person for help in teaching them to you, is that they can open up a whole new world.

Through learning to communicate with people worldwide, you become connected once again, like you were when you were young. You can lose the sense of separation and being left behind that can arise in isolation.

You have been a great advocate for this for many years now, Will. My wife, Kathy heard you speak at a seminar years ago about this and learned more when she later helped edit your book *Life Expectancy*. Your passion and advocacy in urging older people to get up to speed with "modern" communications devices personally inspired her!

She looked at me one day back then and said, "He's right! It's just being comfortable with what I have been doing that keeps me resistant to the vastly improved solutions out there today. I'm committed to keeping up." She got rid of her old (probably first generation) cell phone and got the latest smartphone. She also began adding applications and software on her phone and computer. Today she stays in touch with friends and relatives all over the country and sends pictures and videos to our children and grandchildren with a real sense of fun and entertainment. And she has become confident in her ability to do so.

When there are difficulties around the home, or in the garden, or with insects or animals in the yard, or when minor ailments hit us, she's on Google immediately finding solutions. The other day, I almost called an expensive plumber to come to our home to fix a broken toilet fixture. Before I could do it, she said, "Hang on, before you do that, let me see what I can find," and she went online. After Googling the problem, she ordered an inexpensive part from Amazon and fixed it herself after watching a short YouTube "how-to" video tutorial.

Our society has a kind of ingrained mythology about old people being unable to learn and "keep up." In my father's generation, people were expected to retire and go away from the real world at age 65. They were no longer thought to be useful to their organizations. Then it got worse: Men of that age, through sheer force of tradition, were considered to be (by themselves, especially) "grumpy old men" or "crotchety old codgers."

In 1993, a popular comedy called *Grumpy Old Men* starring Jack Lemmon and Walter Matthau came out. It was such a hit that they made a sequel two years later called *Grumpier Old Men* with the same cast. The movies were funny and popular in part because audiences knew that the grumpiness of old men was a choiceless given.

I catch myself being seduced by the same myth. For example, when Zoom first came out, I was grumpy about it. "I'm in my 70s. I don't need to use stuff like Zoom. I'm old school. I'm low-tech and proud of it. I don't need to be a part of this crazy new world run by young people and their ridiculous futuristic devices. What's wrong with the telephone? Why can't you just call me like we have been doing successfully for a hundred years?"

Like me, too many older people cling to the old folks' slogans that masquerade as wisdom. The one that applies here is, “You can’t teach an old dog, new tricks.” The problem with that “wisdom” is that there’s no truth to it. As we pointed out earlier, dogs can learn new tricks at any age. And so can we—and we can Google how to do them!

Mindful Choice #22

I choose to learn about and use the available communication tools, stay informed about the world around me, and better maintain my health and well-being through digital connections with others.

Conversation Twenty-Three
We Should All Be Coaching Someone

We reaffirm that each person can serve others by sharing their unique knowledge; the science behind our desire to talk about ourselves; and the most potent aspect of quality communication and how to do it better.

Steve

When we suggest that everybody be a coach, we don't mean becoming a full-time coach or consultant who charges high fees and works full time to help individuals and businesses be more successful. That's the work that Will and I have done, and it's taken years to develop that at a professional level.

We mean it more as a simple, compassionate level of interaction with others. At the level of listening to people, encouraging, and mentoring them, and sharing your experiences of life when you think it would help. Really listening!

When we've got a good number of years of experience behind us, we can approach family members, friends, or acquaintances with simple "coaching" offers: "How can I help you with that?" "How might I be of service to you?"

Deep, creative listening is a coach's most vital (and perhaps the most overlooked and neglected) skill at any level. In the

Coaching Prosperity School I founded and led for many years, we spent many hours working on how to listen more deeply and thoroughly to clients and potential clients.

At the beginning of their careers, professional coaches' first impulse is to be overt, even aggressive tellers of what they think they know and what they presume their client needs to hear, and to do it in the context of the coach's worldview! But that presumption and behavior actually work *against* the creation and sense of a safe and trusting relationship between two people. (Who may have just met, no less!)

Many times, the first impulse of a senior citizen is to withdraw into loneliness with the false belief that, "I've got no one to talk to." But they are making the same error that professional coaches make when they focus only on their own voice, their own egos, and their own attempts to instantly make a positive impression.

You may think you have no one to talk to, but there are plenty of people out there who would love to be listened to—an unlimited number, in fact. This is the other, and I believe, *much more powerful* aspect of communication: A speaker without an active listener is a person talking to themselves.

Brenda Ueland is one of my heroes. I revisit her classic book on writing, *If You Want to Write*, at least once a year. She was born in 1891 and lived 94 vibrant, productive years as a journalist and a teacher of writing. But to me, her most inspiring observations were about listening.

> I want to write about the great and powerful thing that listening is, and how we forget it. And how we don't listen to our children, or those we love. And least of all—which is so important, too—to those we do not

> love. But we should. Because listening is a magnetic and strange thing, a creative force. Think how the friends that really listen to us are the ones we move toward, and we want to sit in their radius as though it did us good.

The best coaches I know—the most transformative—are the ones who listen deeply and compassionately. Their wisdom and life experience are offered in the context of what they have listened to, and really heard. It is what is relevant for their client, and that is why they are both there.

Those of us who have life experience (all of us!) can do that. It's what true coaching is all about. And, we don't have to charge for it.

Brenda Ueland also said,

> When we are listened to, it creates us, makes us unfold and expand. Ideas actually begin to grow within us and come to life. It makes people happy and free when they are listened to. And if you are a listener, it is the secret of having a good time in society (because everybody around you becomes lively and interesting), of comforting people, of doing them good.

Being a coach, with or without "official" credentials and professional experience, means listening compassionately, offering encouragement, and sharing helpful advice from your history. As seniors, we have *more* to offer because we have more years of life experience upon which to draw. All of us can coach others through the rest of our lives. And create new connections through a dedication to better listening.

Will

We could have easily called this conversation "Listening: The Ultimate Communication." I have been "directive" as a communicator for much of my life, as those who know me well will attest. I have been so concerned with getting to solutions as quickly as possible that when I think, "I've got it"—meaning the nature of the problem—in the same motion, I start moving in the direction of a solution. There can be several problems with this.

First, I may not fully "get it," meaning a deeper explanation or conversation may be in order. Second, an immediate or close-in solution may not be or lead to the optimal outcome. We all have heard the proverb, "Give a man a fish, and you feed him for a day; teach a man to fish, and you feed him for a lifetime." Educating others in the complete process of inquiry and analysis may be much more important than how quickly you achieve a specific solution. Third, as you have articulated, Steve, people are much more engaged in the communication process when the other party doesn't over speak or cut them off when they are talking.

You probably cannot count the number of times I have jumped in on you while speaking and then eventually said, "I am so sorry Steve, I interrupted you. Please go ahead," or, "I'm sorry, Steve, what were you saying?" By then, we may have lost the rhythm of the interchange. (I am *not* asking you to take your valuable time to go back and count. Let's just agree that it is an embarrassing number.)

As a powerful tool in communication, *listening leverages ego*, the speaker's ego, *not yours*. If given a choice, most people want to be *heard* first and foremost! Understanding this is especially important when you want the other party to trust in you. It is true in any interaction where you hope to convey something important or even engage in conversation.

Here is why we need to appreciate the role of ego in conversation.[68]

> On average, people spend 60 percent of conversations talking about themselves—and this figure jumps to 80 percent when communicating via social media platforms . . . Why, in a world full of ideas to discover, develop, and discuss, do people prefer to spend a majority of their time *talking*, and have it be about them? Recent research suggests a simple explanation: *because it feels good.*
>
> Researchers from the Harvard University Social Cognitive and Affective Neuroscience Lab utilized functional magnetic resonance imaging [to determine] whether talking about the self would correspond with increased neural activity in areas of the brain associated with motivation and reward.
>
> Three neural regions stood out . . . self-disclosure resulted in relatively higher levels of activation in areas of the medial prefrontal cortex (MPFC) generally *associated with self-related thought*. [The other two regions] . . . are generally *associated with reward* and have been linked to the pleasurable feelings and motivational states associated with stimuli such as sex, cocaine, and good food.

> Activation of this system when discussing the self suggests that *self-disclosure*, like other more traditionally recognized stimuli, *may be inherently pleasurable*—and that people may be motivated to talk about themselves more than other topics (no matter how interesting or important these non-self-oriented topics may be). [Emphasis added.]

This reminds me of the humorous comment about a self-absorbed person who had been talking non-stop for 45 minutes and then realized it. "Oh my gosh, enough about me. Tell me, now that you know me better, what do *you think of me*?"

Knowing that we tap into other people's good feelings when talking about themselves and their interests is only part of the equation. To set the table for listening, you must *communicate that your role is listening*, but not by saying it. You make clear through your actions that they are getting your undivided attention.

Whether in-person or on video calls, eliminate the distractions that could suggest you may only be half-listening.

- Remove your smartphone from view. Its mere presence is a disruption to the eye and potentially the ear of the speaker—a time bomb waiting to explode: "How fast do I have to complete my sentence before that thing interrupts me?"
- Put aside any material that may represent a physical barrier between you and the listener. Obstacles that can put off the listener could be a desk, table, or something in front of your screen that can be viewed on theirs (a pile of books, papers, or even a keyboard if intrusive). On

video calls, keep the background behind you simple and soothing.

- Taking an occasional note can confirm that you are listening and that you have heard things that are worthwhile. Alternate between eye contact with your speaker and writing a note now and then. Don't become absorbed in writing everything down. Do not ask permission to take notes on your computer or smartphone. Getting consent doesn't mean it's a good idea. If you want to type a recap, do it later.

Each of these points is a subtle demonstration that your attention is where it will do the most good: not on YOU. The sole focus is on the deep listening that you mentioned, Steve. Undivided attention focused on the most important person in your life at that moment, the person hoping to be seen and heard.

Be prepared to "prime the pump" by having open-ended questions at the ready. These are questions whereby you create space for expansive responses to make clear you are the listener. These will be questions that cannot be fully answered with the words "yes" or "no" or with a short, complete, unambiguous answer ("pastrami on rye with spicy brown mustard, hold the pickle").

Examples of such open-ended questions include, "How are you feeling today?" "What are you struggling with at this point in your life?" "Tell me about any self-limiting beliefs that are getting in your way." "What do you consider your four most important character traits?" Or the time-honored psychiatrist's prompt, "Tell me more about that."

My favorite open-ended question of all time was asked of me

by your coach, Steve Hardison, in the first three seconds after I sat down with him. "*So, how did you come to be here today*?" I marveled (and still do) that such a question could be answered with everything from "I drove my car" or "I took Main Street to the 202 freeway, got off on the 63rd Street exit, and then drove the few blocks to your house," or "It all started when I was living on my grandfather's farm as a five-year-old; his legs got caught up in the combine, the haystack caught on fire, and the seven-year drought came."

Open-ended questions offer you plenty of material to keep the focus on the speaker. If the flow is slowing, you can use follow-up or what I call "booster questions" to keep the speaker moving in the direction of what they are there to get off their chest (though they may not know that's what they're doing).

Examples of booster questions include, "I didn't see that coming. How did that make you feel?" "That makes so much sense! Then what happened?" "I'm very interested in what led up to that incident. Would you mind telling me more about it?" "Very interesting, but could you clarify?" "What did you believe they thought about you after that happened?" "Please don't stop there. Tell me more—please."

Don't interrupt. If a follow-up question arises during your listening, just make a note of it for later.

Your thoughtful consideration of some "opening" questions doesn't just apply to initial conversations. They are just as crucial for developing closer relationships with people you already know whether a significant other, a friend, boss or employee, or a coaching client. Here are some questions that could be used in those contexts:

- What advice would you offer if you could have a conversation with your 21 (or 30, 40, or 50) year-old self?
- What is the most significant risk you've ever taken?
- What is one thing you wouldn't want to live without?
- Who do you count on the most for help?
- How have your priorities changed over the past ten years?
- If money wasn't an issue, what would you do with your time?
- What makes you lose track of time?
- If you had to teach something, what would you teach?
- What would you regret not doing, being, or having in your life?
- What's something about yourself or your life that might surprise others to learn?
- What would you do if you did not care what others thought?
- What's something you'd do even if you never made any money?
- What's something you keep telling yourself you'll do when you retire or when you "have the time"?

We have mentioned throughout this book that being and staying curious is an elixir for mindful aging. It's a way to both create and deepen relationships that can be mutually rewarding. Your preparation and attention are indications that you care enough not to merely fly by the seat of your pants in conversations that matter.

When did you last notice that *your* listening is powerful, and that people want *you* to hear them?

Mindful Choice #23

I choose to actively and deeply listen to (and hear) others as a way of living more fully and serving them with the best of my attention.

Conversation Twenty-Four
The Joy in Pursuing Self-Transformation

We explore the path of self-transformation, consider some characteristics that support the journey toward self-actualization, and confirm the necessity for self-reliance in the process.

Steve

When I give seminars these days, I pay more attention as people first come into the room than I once did. They sit down and look up to the front of the room, and I can see in some of their eyes—they are here for information only.

They have that edgy look. Impatient. Wondering if they should be somewhere else. One last double-thumbing of the smartphone. Now they look pensive. "Did I leave the oven on at home?" "Will I return to an inferno of smoke and ashes instead of my cozy little house?" "Is this seminar a waste of my time? I probably already know this stuff!"

These are the information people.

But who else is in the room?

Oh, there they are: the transformation people.

The transformation people look different. Their eyes are

sparkling with a look of quiet mischief. They laugh with the person sitting next to them. They have one of my books under their chair, and I notice it has many of those little colored stickers coming out of the pages, some pale blue, some pale yellow, and some pink.

Their eyes are clear. They are feeling something good. Maybe it's *possibility*. They wouldn't mind being a little intoxicated by that today. The possibility of lasting, meaningful transformation.

Through my years of coaching people into and through personal transformation, the key difference between these two "types" of people was the relationship they had developed with positive change.

Our conversations have been about the possibility of real change and true transformation in the ways we view aging, and the possibility of having the rest of our lives actually become the best of our lives.

But that means taking full responsibility for the desired change. Not having someone else be responsible for shifting my life for the better but cultivating self-reliance and taking personal ownership for making these changes through mindful choices.

Advocating self-reliance could sound contradictory to the many times we've suggested reaching out and asking for help, forming alliances, creating networks of support. But it isn't a contradiction. In the heart of it, you have to be *willing* to reach out. You must own it.

I remember once complaining to my psychologist, Nathaniel Branden, that I was a victim of my circumstances in life. My then-wife had entered an institution for a brain disorder, and I was awarded full custody of our four young children for raising on my own. I was living in debt in a run-down little house and transporting my kids in a beater of an old car.

He said, "How would your life be different if you took full responsibility for your standard of living?" He again had me give him six quick completions to this sentence stem: "If I took full responsibility for my standard of living, I would . . ." He did that because he wanted the answers to be mine, coming from my own brain and imagination, not advice from him on what to do next. I wrote down my answers, kept my lists, and acted upon as many ideas as I could. It wasn't long before my standard of living began to shift in a positive direction.

In our society and the history of using language, "taking responsibility" has mostly negative connotations. It is mainly associated with bad choices and even crimes. For example, the phrase "You are responsible for that!" means you are to blame and should be ashamed because you didn't step up to it.

But true responsibility means "willingness and ability to respond." When you take responsibility for how you will live the rest of your life, you receive the energy and inspiration that comes with being a creator. The more self-reliance I cultivate, especially in my later years, the more power and autonomy I experience and the more I can, paraphrasing Gandhi, *be* the change I want to *see* in my world.

And again, self-reliance does not mean isolation or withdrawal from the human community. The more autonomy and self-reliance I develop, the easier it is to reach out to, be welcomed by, and serve others.

Will

After listening to you talk about the distinction between the people in the room being information or transformation seekers, I have a few thoughts.

At the level of consciousness, they are all information people. Each of them is there to gather information. Each of the listeners has the power to act on what they hear. They can and will make decisions about what to use, store, or discard. They weigh your information in part based upon your reputation and how you say what you have to say. Though more intangible, this is information too.

The transformation people arrive in the room with a strong sense of who they are today and a context for the change they are seeking. They are settling into their seats with openness and purpose as well. Whether it is your information or other inputs, these seekers come into the venue looking for what you might offer to help them transform into who they are becoming. It isn't just the information they're seeking; they are looking for direct or indirect clues—bits of insight—to help propel them forward on their journeys into "what's next."

The transformation-seekers know that when they set a direction and a context for living, the world will move for them, whether they see and feel each input or slight shift or not. The objective doesn't have to be end-game consequential. It could be more akin to the power of intention we discussed earlier. "I will raise my awareness of the value of each person I meet," or "I intend to notice and appreciate my natural surroundings," or "I want to notice when I feel happy and satisfied and celebrate those moments."

But then again, by aiming high—as in, "I choose to pursue self-actualization," it could be that the path, and the tools needed to get there, will be revealed. This is very exciting.

The term "self-actualization" is a familiar one, however, it is worth settling on a definition for our purposes here. When we use the term, we mean the realization of a person's potential, the desire to accomplish everything that one can, to become the most that one can be. As said by Abraham Maslow, it is a desire "to become everything one is capable of becoming."[69] A person comes to find a meaningful life in ways that are important to them. [Maslow, through research, identified fifteen characteristics of a self-actualized person. You can review these in the endnote, if interested.[70]]

You may not be aware, Steve, that Maslow was developing what might have been his most transformative work when he died at 62. He was working on a theory linking self-actualization to self-transcendence and spirituality. In a sense, it seems he was "going bigger." A brief description of it fits perfectly here, providing more insight into the transformation-seekers and the journey toward integration and wholeness.

Scott Barry Kaufman writes in Scientific American,[71]

> Maslow's emphasis [at the time of his death] was less on a rigid hierarchy of needs and more on the notion that self-actualized people are motivated by health, growth, wholeness, integration, humanitarian purpose, and the "real problems of life."

* * *

After rigorous testing, I found that ten of Maslow's proposed characteristics of self-actualization stand up to scientific scrutiny:

- Continued Freshness of Appreciation - "I can appreciate again and again… the basic goods of life… however stale these experiences may have become to others."

- Acceptance - "I accept all of my quirks and desires without shame or apology."

- Authenticity - "I can maintain my dignity and integrity even in environments and situations that are undignified."

- Equanimity - "I tend to take life's inevitable ups and downs with grace, acceptance, and equanimity."

- Purpose - "I feel a great responsibility and duty to accomplish a particular mission in life."

- Efficient Perception of Reality - "I am always trying to get at the real truth about people and nature."

- Humanitarianism – "I have a genuine desire to help the human race."

- Peak Experiences - "I often have experiences in which I feel new horizons and possibilities opening up for myself and others."

- Good Moral Intuition - "I can tell 'deep down' right away when I've done something wrong."
- Creative Spirit - "I have a generally creative spirit that touches everything I do."

> I found an overall pattern suggesting that the characteristics of self-actualization lead to optimal health and growth.
>
> Overall, self-actualization was related to higher levels of stability and the ability to protect your highest-level goals from disruption by distracting impulses and thoughts. Self-actualization was related to lower levels of disruptive impulsivity . . . nonconstructive thinking . . . and a lack of authenticity and meaning.
>
> Just as Maslow predicted, those with higher self-actualization scores were much more motivated by growth, exploration, and love of humanity than the fulfillment of deficiencies in basic needs. What's more, self-actualization scores were associated with multiple indicators of well-being, including greater life satisfaction, curiosity, self-acceptance, positive relationships, environmental mastery, personal growth, autonomy, and purpose in life. [Emphasis added.]

When you, Steve, distinguish information gatherers from those who have set a transformational direction, you can see the difference in the resonance of your message and what to expect in the nature of their comments and questions.

Personal transformation is a process of expanding consciousness through "self-work." We become more aware of old and new self-views and the value of integrating them into our evolving self-definition—the one that is the result of our transformation-seeking.[72] It is a journey for the self-reliant. So why shouldn't more of us reach for the stars in Maslow's evolved model of self-actualization? It could be the cherry on top of our best self-care, coming at a time when these considerations can be front and center for us.

As with many of the choices on our list (not all), there is no wrong answer, and most can be easily modified. If you choose to live as an information gatherer, it is a way of extending what you know into the future, believing that the information will continue to apply. If you choose a path of transformation, you open yourself to looking at the world based upon inputs (and your reactions to them) that light and enlighten your direction.

As we age, we have the possibility of proactively harnessing both information and transformation as ways of being in the world. The essence of the self-reliance that you referenced earlier, Steve, is this.

Mindful Choice #24

I commit to being my best self, intentionally pursuing self-transformation through a commitment to self-reliance and engaging with others.

Conversation Twenty-Five
Passion: Fuel for Living

We explore the passions that can fuel love for learning and activities, why these interests are essential at every age, and trying something new to stay fresh for living.

Will

The mention of passion may bring up thoughts of budding romance, roses, candlelight, being oblivious to surroundings, and unmistakable stirrings of desire. The sizzling of romantic electricity is in the air.

It probably won't surprise you though that the origin of the word passion was from the Latin "passio," a word for suffering. Found in the writings of Plato (429-347 BC) and Spinoza (1632-1677)[73] were suggestions that passion involves a loss of reason and control. The gist of it, in plain English, is that people afflicted with passion may experience a kind of suffering, as if they were slaves to their passion.

But I digress. This conversation is not about that kind of passion.

There is a dimension to *motivation* that includes passion. There is a psychological tie between passion and the highest levels of achievement. Many "creative types" discover this passion early in life and can end up dedicating their entire lives to pursuing mastery in their chosen field. It could be painting, sculpture, composing music, writing, or a myriad of other arts. Passion for creating is, of course, not limited to the arts. For many, the rewards are primarily psychic, not recognition or money. Passion drives their pursuit of excellence, and most other things come second—perhaps including making a living or developing relationships with others.

I have been a business leader for most of my life. I would say that I was committed, dedicated, hardworking, and purposeful. But I don't recall describing my feeling for what I was doing as "passionate."

The fact that I didn't connect the concept of passion to it did not mean I wasn't constantly striving to improve and refine my skills and build on my knowledge. I did that in spades, often with obsession. I know many can relate.

Furthermore, my comments don't suggest that many entrepreneurs and other committed businesspeople do not possess a passion for what they do that is equivalent to that of great creative artists.

I have learned that, in addition to the kind of passion defined as "ardent affection" or a "strong amorous feeling or desire," there is another form of it—that which we tap into relating to our *activities*. We all explore our environments and ourselves through education, work, spirituality, relationships, and virtually every other part of living. R. J. Vallerand writes,

> "Of these [activities], only a few will be perceived as particularly enjoyable, important, and to have some resonance with how people see themselves. From these few activities one or two will eventually be preferred

> and engaged in on a regular basis and turn out to be passionate. Thus, passion [is defined] as a strong inclination toward a self-defining activity that one likes (or even loves), finds important, and in which one invests time and energy on a regular basis." [74]

I have heard people described by statements like, "She is so passionate about teaching, she never stops making an effort to get better." Or, "He is passionate about his collection of South Pacific indigenous art objects. His knowledge and collection continue to multiply. Don't get him started talking about it." This kind of passion can be tied to work, hobbies, avocations, volunteering, caregiving—anything that is an activity, not a "strong, amorous desire" for another person.

But an activity pursued with passion, ". . . is not simply an activity that one loves dearly, values highly, and engages in on a regular basis. It is also something that comes to define oneself. The activity becomes an inherent part of who the person is . . . It is something that can come to define you, in part"[75]. The activity is merged into the individual. In response to the question, "Who are you?" this person may say, "I am a songwriter," or "I am an athlete." His work may be plumbing, but the question wasn't "What do you *do*?"

This kind of passion,

> . . . produces a motivational force to engage in the activity willingly and engenders a sense of volition and personal endorsement about pursuing the activity . . . individuals do not experience an uncontrollable urge to engage in the passionate activity, but rather freely choose to do so. With this type of passion, the activity occupies a significant but not overpowering space in the

person's identity and is in harmony with other aspects of the person's life.[76]

In other words, passion isn't an obsession, but it IS integral to feeling alive. It is a source of energy and happiness. It balances other aspects of life that may not have the same effect.

I have had several of these passions. When I was in my teens and 20s, it was, "I am an athlete." When I had homes with a yard, "I am a landscaper and gardener." When I discovered snow skiing at 50, "I am a skier." It was an accessible and fulfilling activity, at the time, genuinely engaged with passion.

Over the past decade, and more so in the past couple of years, I have found a passion for writing. Though I am often "working" at other things that sometimes take most of my time, I am energized, expanding, and passionate when I write. "I am a writer."

A passion for an activity adds interest and meaning to living. There is life energy in being passionate about something. It needn't be obsessively pursued to add to feelings of engagement, happiness, and accomplishment.

What makes you smile when you see or hear about it? Animals, walking, the beach, hiking, playing bridge, redesigning your living space, cooking, tending to plants and flowers, following baseball, opera, blues, country, reading, church activities, museums, traveling? These are just a few of the many options of activities that might have a seed of passion for you.

In our senior years of living, the discovery of new activities (even simply to sample or try) can lead you to passions that may light up the rest of your days. Pursued with some energy and regularity, you could find yourself thriving in new and different ways. Your psychology will continue to shift in the direction of well-being. Your brain function will improve. You might even decrease the number of screen hours per day spent watching other people's lives.

And I almost forgot to mention that for most of my life, if my significant activities didn't have an element of financial compensation to them, I wasn't nearly as interested. Of course, there were some exceptions, but I was motivated by monetary compensation. I never understood until now why people drank up what I thought was the new-age Kool-Aid of "Do what you love, the money will follow."

Today, I am doing what I love, and I have no idea if any money will follow. I know that having a passion for writing at this point in my life has me thinking differently about money. "What do I need to earn to keep pursuing my passion?" is, for me, a very different lens for viewing life than, "If it doesn't have compensation associated with it, I'm not interested."

It would have been nice to see this possibility before six decades had passed. But then again, being fully awake at any age is powerful and enabling.

Steve

My experience matches yours on this, Will. My current passions came in what people who fixate on the limited linear notions of time would call "later in life."

Motivational speakers and gurus in the self-help field often ask, "What's your passion?" then urge you to, "Do that! Follow your passion!"

That would lead to many in their audience (especially me) feeling left out if they couldn't locate their passion. "Hey, loser, you should be able to point to it! It's in there somewhere, like your liver or your spleen. Point to it! Then follow it!"

I still can't point to where my spleen is. But passion, I have found—and so many of the people I work with have found—can arise unexpectedly. And it can be developed and cultivated. It comes from a willingness to try stuff. To explore.

Michael Jordan's passion as a young athlete was baseball. It was his sport. People urged him to try basketball. He might be good at that, too, and he could play it in the off-season. He tried it and liked it well enough but was cut from his high school team. The amazing Michael Jordan—the same Michael Jordan who is, today, synonymous with basketball greatness and superstardom—at one time wasn't even good enough to play high school basketball!

But he was willing to keep trying, and the better he got, the more passion he felt for the game. The rest, of course, is sports history. His pre-existing feeling for the game was non-existent, but the more he played, the more it was cultivated and developed. And he *worked* at it—as hard as any athlete in history. But for him, it was an expression of passion for what he loved.

No matter how old we are, we all have latent passion inside us, waiting to be recognized, developed, and cultivated.

Oscar-winner (for *The Paper Chase*) John Houseman became passionate about acting but didn't try it out until he was in his 80s. The famous folk artist Anna Mary Moses (later known as Grandma Moses) began painting at the age of 78. Her well-known painting *Sugaring Off* was posthumously sold for $1.2 million.

My passion for playing piano and singing with it was non-existent until my late 60s when we inherited the beautiful Steinway baby grand piano I mentioned earlier. We thought it would look good in the living room. I thought people would consider us classy and cultured when they visited . . . as long as they didn't ask us to play anything.

But, as I said earlier, I had enough interest in learning to play to keep at it. The more I learned and practiced, the more I liked it. Soon I was really loving it, and that love evolved slowly to a full-on passion. Today I can't walk by a piano without a significant urge to go over to it and play.

So, there's a progression available to anyone at any age. It starts with a mild interest, followed by a willingness to try stuff, followed by getting good enough to enjoy repeating it, followed by loving it and bringing that love to every encounter with it, ending up as a full-blown passion.

Bring enough love to *anything*—whether it's an activity, a person, or a historical or scientific subject of study, and you can find yourself happily in a state of life-giving, life-enhancing, life-saving passion.

Mindful Choice #25

I will actively pursue and discover new passions in my life by trying new things and deepening my interest in existing activities.

Conversation Twenty-Six
Let Nature Fill You Up

We find agreement that experiencing nature is both inspiring and reassuring through our simple observation of and presence in it.

Will

The movie *Nomadland* won Oscars for Best Picture, Best Actress (Frances McDormand), and Best Director (Chloé Zhao). Zhao also wrote the screenplay based on the book *Nomadland: Surviving America in the Twenty-First Century* by Jessica Bruder.[77]

The antiseptic one-sentence summary is that Fern (McDormand), a woman in her 60s, reacts to widowhood and the economic shutdown of her Nevada town by moving into her Ford Econoline van and taking to the highways. The movie is visceral and moving while exploring sadness, unease, and an inside view of a nomadic, self-sufficient group of Americans with little by way of material possessions.

I lived on the Navajo Indian Reservation in Kayenta, Arizona, for three years when I was growing up. The Navajo Nation covers about 17,544,500 acres (27,000 square miles—about the size of West Virginia), but fewer than 175,000 people live within its borders (6.4 people per square mile).

Kayenta is about 30 miles from Monument Valley Navajo Tribal Park (home of the sandstone Mitten Buttes) and 80 miles from the only place where four states meet (Arizona, Colorado, New Mexico, and Utah, creatively named "Four Corners").

As a middle-schooler at the time, and new to the locale, this was my first up-close view of mind-blowing wild, beautiful, and epically large country. High desert, reddish-colored, natural sandstone sculptures, canyons, cliffs, gnarly piñon pines, forested mesas, wind, sand of all colors, and endless skies—day and night. Miles and miles of what many people would describe as emptiness or desolation.

Simply being in a place like this filled my senses and my heart. I knew it, and I was an 11-year-old kid. Some people might have this feeling standing on a rooftop in New York City (which I have done). It, too, is unique—but for me very much unlike the magnificence of natural creations.

The movie *Nomadland* has this kind of natural grandeur as the backdrop for its story about people challenged by financial shortcomings, family disconnectedness, and the search for simple living among kindred spirits. The movie is somewhat bleak and downbeat, though it portrays real-life themes with truth.[78] And it delivers images of our country in its vastness, natural and sometimes desolate beauty.

If you have been unaware of these potential gifts to your senses or unable to travel to access them, take a first step and drink up the images in this film. The places are not household names for the most part. Nevada's Black Rock Desert. The Badlands of South Dakota. The Scottsbluff area of Nebraska. Quartzsite, Arizona in the Sonoran Desert. The San Bernardino

National Forest (east of Los Angeles). And the perhaps better-known shoreline and crashing waves of Point Arena in Mendocino County, California.

You can access these and other places like them all over our country. Besides the travel and related costs, you can see and experience these natural works of art for free, or for modest admission fees. If you have never been filled up by the vastness and soul-touching experience of bigger-than-life natural creations, you are missing something that will enrich your existence. I don't know what heaven is, but I believe heaven-on-earth exists in these magnificent and accessible places.

"The stars awaken a certain reverence, because though always present, they are inaccessible; but all natural objects make a kindred impression when the mind is open to their influence."

~Ralph Waldo Emerson

A memorable monologue in *Nomadland* conveys this sense of reverence and being filled to the brim with it. The actor is an authentic American nomad nicknamed Swankie. She describes a closer-up view within the immense vistas I mentioned. She says,

> I'm gonna be 75 this year. I think I've lived a pretty good life. I've seen some really neat things kayaking all of those places. And . . . you know, like a moose in the wild. A moose family on the river in Idaho, and big white pelicans landed just six feet over my kayak on a lake in Colorado. Or . . . come around a bend, was a cliff and find hundreds and hundreds of swallow nests on the

> wall of the cliff. And the swallows flying all around and reflecting in the water. So, it looks like I'm flying with the swallows and they're under me, and over me, and all around me. And little babies are hatching out, and eggshells are falling out of the nests landing on the water and floating on the water. These little white shells. That was like, it's just so awesome. I felt like I've done enough. My life was complete. If I died right then, at that moment, would be perfectly fine.[79]

Films and photos can show the way. But standing in those places and capturing your own "mind-movie" (as described by Swankie) of the expansiveness and one-of-a-kind beauty is like bathing in the infinite. We all can access this expansiveness if we look.

Steve

For many years of my life, I didn't appreciate nature at all. It was lovely but insignificant as I pursued happiness and "success" and fame as a songwriter, and the money. As you mentioned—*always* the money. It wasn't until I crashed and burned enough times that I finally realized I was going down the wrong road.

I know that by being on the right spiritual path and reframing the anxiety associated with "achievement," one can be more open to the fulfillment and joy nature has to offer. You did this at a young age with your fortunate introduction to some of those spaces on the Navajo Nation.

For me, my appreciation for nature has come much later in

life, as I learned to relax and be at peace and feel gratitude for things outside my ego.

I love the choice you recommend here, Will, to commune more with nature as we age, not less. Of course, one can choose to do either, but not exploring the outdoors gives up a treat for your soul. Choosing *more* can be done by venturing out to encounter nature's life-affirming beauty on a majestic, jaw-dropping scale as you talk about, or on the smallest level, like keeping house plants watered, witnessed, and even "talked to"!

Gardening columnist Adrian Higgins wrote a moving piece about this in the *Washington Post.*[80] His article features the great poet Stanley Kunitz who lived in a small house in Provincetown, Massachusetts. There, he gently, but lovingly and obsessively ". . . had turned a sandy slope into a three-tiered ornamental garden, anchored by conifers, then richly planted as a flower garden."

Higgins went on to say, "Kunitz seemed to draw such energy from the garden that he became almost comically blithe to his advanced age. When he was 95, he became the nation's poet laureate. At 98, he decided to take down a mature spruce tree, so he could replant an area of the garden. At the end of each growing season, he would turn to (poet and gardening expert) Genine Lentine to contemplate what to plant the following year. Together, they wrote *The Wild Braid: A Poet Reflects on a Century in the Garden,* published in 2005."

In a conversation with Kunitz, Lentine made an observation that really stood out for me. She said, "A lot of poets walk around, asking: 'How do we survive, how do we thrive, how do we flourish?' And the garden takes us through those questions."

I can choose to ignore the truth and beauty of nature. Just as

I can choose not to ask myself how I might thrive and flourish by creating a well-attended garden. But the choice you offer here is better. Using nature as my inspiration, I could actually get closer to the mindset of Stanley Kunitz, and maybe even have my gravestone say, "He was comically blithe to his advanced age."

Mindful Choice #26

I will appreciate nature, in both its untamed and domestic forms, and allow it to fill me up as only it can.

Conversation Twenty-Seven
This Is the Day the Lord Has Made

We share what we have learned from those who serve people near the end of life and talk about being powerfully in this moment without fear of the next.

Steve

A couple of decades ago, I worked as a speaker and seminar leader, teaching courses in time management, goal-setting and achievement, communication, and the like. One day, a seminar I gave in Scottsdale to a group of nurses changed my life in a major way.

This particular nursing group worked with patients with advanced stages of cancer, and a large percentage of their patients were terminally ill. *Oh, my goodness*, I thought. *These poor nurses not only have challenging but probably depressing jobs. I don't envy the work they do. Maybe my seminar can help give them a bit of a boost.*

When I arrived in the conference room, I noticed something odd as the nurses came in and took their seats. It looked as though they were *cheerful*. They were chatting with each other, smiling, and I even heard laughter.

Was I in the right place? Apparently so, because my name

was on the whiteboard underneath a very colorfully scripted "WELCOME," and some of the nurses were holding a copy of my book. I concluded that this must be the right place.

The seminar flowed along nicely, and the question-and-answer period at the end was lively and upbeat. After it was over, a number of the nurses hung around to have me sign books and chat. But I just had to ask them, "What's the deal with how happy you guys all seem to be? I've never had such an upbeat group before. Is it just such a relief to come in here and get away from the difficult work you have to do with terminal patients?"

One of the older nurses said, "We don't find our work difficult. It's very uplifting. The patients we work with are inspiring to us. Their attitudes are amazing."

The others saw my puzzled face, but they were nodding in agreement. The older nurse quickly realized she would have to explain her remarks to me, and as she did, I took my notebook out to write down what she was saying.

I still have the notebook today, and when I take it out to look at it (which I do every so often as a reminder), I can see some of it is illegible because I was writing as fast as I could.

"Of course, it doesn't happen right away," she said. "But our patients, almost every one of them, arrive at a certain kind of peace about their prognosis. It's a kind of acceptance. They know they don't have long to live. Sometimes they have only days or weeks. But something happens. I don't know quite what it is; maybe it's that time becomes more precious. Maybe their appreciation of life in the moment deepens. Who can say what it really is? But they are peaceful and even happy, strange as that must sound. And they are a joy to work with, and most of us who may have dreaded this kind of nursing assignment end up never wanting to leave here."

Years later, after I'd done a lot of work with the guidance of an enlightened spiritual teacher, I learned from his teaching, and ultimately from personal experience, that we humans are happiest when we are living in the "now." Not worried about the future (it could be full of fear) or brooding about the past (a life that could be recalled with remorse and regret). We are most "complete" when we are fully present in the current moment.

It's the difference between seeing time as a gift and seeing time as something "being lost." And it isn't just older people who experience time as a problem. Many of the younger "high achievers" I coach and consult with today are very resistant to my recommendation to "slow down." To them, slowing down means falling behind.

Living in the now sounds easy, but it really isn't. We have been conditioned to achieve, produce, and perform to "get ahead" and win the praise and approval of others.

Fortunately, there is a workable midway system that will get you headed in that direction. I first learned it in addiction recovery meetings where one of the well-known mantras is facing life "One Day at a Time." When faced with the terrifying prospect of never being able to drink again, my sponsor would say, "This program isn't asking you to do that. Or even think about doing that. We just ask that you not drink *today*. Can you do that?"

Of course, I could do that. Just one day. A recovery program designed *just for today*. That was doable. And that is why it worked. Here I am, four decades later, clean and sober, not having had a drink during the days since Day One, and it was all done by simply staying with it one day at a time.

Later, I learned something profound said by the most successful college basketball coach of all time, UCLA's John Wooden. He coached his teams to more national championships than any other coach, before or since. His philosophy? "Make each day your masterpiece." He taught his players to treat each day as if it were the only day. For them, a Wednesday afternoon in the practice gym was as important to their growth as players as the day of a national championship game.

I have heard many gospel and even rock versions of the song (inspired by a Bible passage[81]) called "This Is the Day the Lord Has Made." One doesn't have to subscribe to any particular religion to feel the power in that. THIS IS THE DAY. It's an unusual way to live, to wake up each morning and fully realize that THIS is the day I've been given to live in and lean into.

Here are some of the lyrics from "This Is the Day the Lord Has Made," from a version written by Fred Hammond:

> Now we serve notice to depression, confusion
> All manner of evil and every sickness
> You came in to bind but you cannot stay
> 'Cause the people of God we ain't havin' it.
> It's a good day, even though I cried last Tuesday
> And I was out of cash by Friday
> No matter what comes next, I'm gonna stand up
> And give him the praise 'cause this is the day.
> This is the day, this is the day
> That the Lord has made, that the Lord has made
> I will rejoice, I will rejoice
> And be glad in it, glad in it.

I want to see *this day* as if it were my whole life in a microcosm. I am born when I wake up in the morning, and I peacefully cross over into sleep at night.

My bucket list is no longer some future possibility wish list about climbing mountains, swimming with dolphins, playing drums with the Rolling Stones, dancing on stage with Jennifer Lopez, or throwing out the first pitch on opening day at Yankee Stadium.

My bucket list is one of improved well-being each day through the choices I can make today: play music, move my body, do some reading in a great book, call a friend to cheer him up, do some work in the garden, write a chapter for my book, love and serve the people I care about.

A great day is the same thing as a great life, and you said, Will, we don't have to travel to Tibet to discover it.

Life isn't linear. It isn't a cluster of accumulations strung out over time. Life isn't made up of memories and future worries and plans; it just feels that way to those of us unwilling to live one day at a time and realize that THIS is the day that life is made of.

Will

I'm inspired by your words and think you should make a YouTube video playing and singing a joyful version of *This is the Day the Lord Has Made* on your piano. Maybe you can Zoom in the Skagit Valley Chorale as the gospel chorus for the refrain. Keep it in mind!

You won't believe this. Or maybe you will and simply say, "There are no accidents!" Just yesterday, before we had this conversation, I was fortunate to meet Cheryl, a registered nurse

(RN) who is nearing 60. It turned out that she is a hospice nurse.

Hospice is a type of health care that prioritizes comfort and quality of life by reducing pain and suffering for terminally ill patients. It isn't considered "giving up" but rather turning the focus to the patient's quality of life and providing the support needed to live the remainder of life as comfortably as possible.

Hospice is holistic care, addressing needs from managing pain and symptoms to providing emotional, social, and spiritual support. This service is usually provided by a team that includes a personal (attending) physician, specialized hospice nurses, aides, physical therapists, social workers, and chaplains or the equivalent.

Cheryl has been a nurse for over 15 years, but since she was a child, she has always felt called to work with people approaching death. As a girl who had never experienced the loss of a loved one, she isn't sure why she had the feeling and was never sure how it might unfold. But the feeling never went away. Cheryl was a surgical nurse and administrator for much of her career, but she recently realized her calling and has worked as a hospice nurse for a few months now.

What's even more interesting is that she is a hospice *admitting nurse* who makes house calls. She goes to the patients' homes and leads the meeting with the patient, family, and other interested parties. This gathering is a delicate moment of truth. Moving to hospice care is saying "no" to any potential medical solutions. It acknowledges the nearing of the end of their Earthly existence.

Just as was the case with the cancer ward nurses you met, Cheryl discovered these patients were, for the most part, ready, resolved, at peace, and not resisting the process.

I asked her a similar question to the one you put to the nurses: "How can you possibly leave your work at the 'office'? By the time you get home, you must be ragged. I can't imagine confronting the life-and-death circumstances you do each day and then making dinner, relaxing with a Netflix series, or taking a walk."

She said, "This is the work I've felt destined to do. It is purely about delivering comfort, concern, and love for the patients and their families and friends. How better could I spend my days? I learn and receive much more from them while they are living the last days and hours of life than I could possibly give."

Meeting Cheryl and hearing her story reminded me of the love known as agape. It is considered the highest form of love—unconditional love. It is described as self-sacrificing love manifested through *conscious service* and *charity*—the voluntary giving of help to those in need.

It's an interesting commentary that the people serving at the passing of others feel fulfilled—more positive and energized in their own lives. I cannot imagine a more compelling call to serve others while you can.

Perhaps consider volunteering at a hospice to sit with those without families and friends. You may learn something akin to what the nurses who deal with terminally ill patients have: Helping people in need at the approach of their final breath is giving and receiving at its highest level. Each is serving the other as part of the same experience. You may even gain insights that will help you when your own time comes.

Before we parted ways, I asked Cheryl what she had learned about how people confront their final moments of living. She said, "What I have seen over and over is that people die as they have lived. If they were centered, loving people, gentle of spirit, kind, and thoughtful of the needs of others, they approach or even welcome their moment of crossing over. But, on the other hand, if they were difficult, angry, self-centered, "half-empty-glass" kind of people, they will say they don't deserve this end, and they resist. Even if they have pain medication and sedatives, their negative energy shows through right up to the end."

No matter your religious or spiritual beliefs, race, education, family, material possessions and wealth, or attitudes—eventually, each of our "buckets" is kicked away for good. But, in the meantime, we have the choice to value each day, as you say, Steve, moment by moment, including our very last one. It is our choice to live *right now*.

Mindful Choice #27

I will find ways to be of service to others today, where I am, without expectation of anything but the opportunity to give. I choose to live in each moment of now, bringing my attention to it and appreciating all the juice in it.

Conversation Twenty-Eight
"Regrets? Too Few to Mention."

We make the case that regret is best served by refusing to indulge it and instead focusing on living and creating today.

Will

When I was a kid, someone invited me to put my index fingers in a device I later learned was a Chinese finger trap, or Chinese handcuffs. I obliged, and once my fingers were in, they were stuck. My first reaction was to pull my fingers out quickly. But the device was woven of pliable bamboo designed to hold your fingers tighter if you resisted. Resistance worked against you and kept your fingers stuck until you were able to push them forward (against your better instincts) and relax them.

Harboring regrets can have the same effect. They can keep you stuck in your resistance to letting them go. Is there anything worse than finding that your thoughts are tinged with regret when you recall certain people and events in your life? Anger or unkindness toward another being, human or otherwise? Things left unsaid to a person no longer here? Quitting when you might have stayed the course? Friendships left untended or abandoned? Thinking back on these moments can feed sentiments like, "I wish I had . . ." or "If only . . ." or "My life would be so different today if . . ."

Some regrets are capable of resolution after the fact, even if years have passed. If a regret is a matter of things said or unsaid, or done or not done, and relate to a person who is still living, you can choose to take action. Make a call or arrange a visit with the person and apologize or do or say what you wish you had done or said at the time. The reaction you receive may be quite different than it would have been the first time around—but if it allows for moving past a regretful memory, it is a way of doing so. You can mark it off your list of re-do's.

Regret as a passing notion is inevitable. Reminiscing—revisiting your past through subjective recall—can be enjoyed as a fond remembrance or a reminder of lessons learned. The memory may arise accompanied by a wince or a sigh, perhaps even a tear.

Full-blown regrets that are incapable of resolution today are another matter altogether. These get their power from today's energy. You spend it as though it can breathe life into something that passed in your life's wake, perhaps without even the barest of recognition. Maybe if you can force a resolution in your own mind, you can eradicate its tentacles from around your heart and brain. Maybe.

Imagine your life not hanging onto regrets. Or at least as Frank Sinatra sang, "too few to mention." If there are things about which you have feelings of regret today, or which you can imagine feeling regret about in the future, it is your choice to deal with them now, once and for all. You can make a list. You can turn your thoughts into paragraphs or pages. Write them down. Look hard at them. Feel them.

Then crumple up the paper and throw it away or dig a hole and bury it.

In terms of past regrets, anything that takes away from your connection to the present bears a cost that should have been paid when it was right in front of you. Living a life without regrets now, means living your life in the present *as* the present.

Should regret be indulged? The question to ask is, "Is this thought, action, or emotion, in my best interest today?" Release the sense that the life you *didn't* experience (due to actions you took or didn't take) would have been better than the one you did. This can be a cleansing experience. Will you spend your energy in the present or remain a prisoner of the past?

Steve

It took much spiritual practice and study to realize the real problem behind the mood-lowering habit of harboring regrets. However, I never had any thoughts that regrets were healthy or life-enhancing in any way. The way my body and emotions reacted to dwelling on some regrets gave me enough negative feedback to know that.

If you drink something toxic and feel intense pain and nausea, you realize right away, "This can't be good for me." If you put your finger in a flame as a child, you quickly understand it isn't safe to do so. It hurts!

So then, why does the mind continue to clutch past regrets?

It does so (and this is just my experience) because we believe that happiness and inner peace come from outside activities and material things, not the spirit that dwells within. If I meditate upon thoughts like, "I really regret not going to art school, or marrying Jennifer, or joining the army, or taking the piano lessons I was offered . . ." I only do so because, deep down, I still believe that not taking actions or making other choices "back then" somehow affects my current level of peace, happiness, and self-satisfaction.

As you suggest, Will, we permit ourselves to believe that the life we *didn't* experience might have been better than the one we got!

As the gifted spiritual teacher Rupert Spira says in his profound and simple book, *Ashes of Love*, "The discovery that peace, happiness, and love are ever-present within our being, and are completely available at every moment of experience, under all conditions, is the most important discovery that anyone can make."

The belief that "I would have been happier today IF . . ." is at the heart of all regret. But that belief is pure ego. Because the ego only knows pride and shame about past actions and acquisitions. It has no connection to our higher, wiser inner spirit.

Not to mention this: You don't ever really *know* whether past regrets (that now only exist as faded, increasingly inaccurate memories) were simply there to kick your butt and wake you up to a better, more authentic path in life—maybe the one you are living today!

Regret is an unnecessary, toxic addiction that hits older people harder than others because the myth of aging that you're believing ("life is over . . . I had my shot and blew it") weakens your will to pursue and discover true happiness in the Now.

I love Alan Watts' metaphor of the boat's wake. He wrote,

> We think that the world is limited and explained by its past. We tend to think that what happened in the past determines what is going to happen next, and we do not see that it is exactly the other way around! What is always the source of the world is the present; the past doesn't explain a thing. The past trails behind the present like the wake of a ship and eventually disappears.

Giving power to regrets in the present is believing that the wake the boat is leaving behind is what is powering it. But the boat represents the Now, the present moment—IT is what is powering us into the future. Regrets are part of the wake and eventually disappear.

Mindful Choice #28

I accept the learning from what I have experienced in my life to date, including feelings of regret, but choose to put my energy into creating today.

Conversation Twenty-Nine
Surviving Death

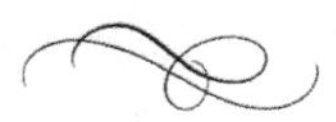

We review the similarities in the recollections of those reporting near-death experiences and the insights revealed through them. We further explore the question, "What if we are not human beings having a spiritual experience but spiritual beings having a human experience?"

Steve

My good friend Michael Neill is an internationally known public speaker (please watch his humorous and profound TEDx Talk on YouTube called "Why Aren't We Awesomer?"[82]), a bestselling author and transformative life and business coach. He and I have done live seminars together and have co-created video master classes on creative writing and financial freedom. Michael is an energetic dervish of optimism who never fails to inspire me and millions of others with his great wit and deep compassion.

Michael is, however, a skeptic in the best sense of the word. He doesn't suffer New Age fools gladly. He holds his work to a high standard of alignment with truth and reality, and he tests it with direct and valid human experience. In addition, he has a sharp wit, a reliable human phoniness detector, and an aversion to anyone peddling false hope.

That's why I was startled when he told me he would collaborate with Anita Moorjani[83] to do some live seminars and create a video program with her called "Experiencing God."

What? That's not the Michael I know and love. His coaching and writing have always been as clear as glass. The psychological grounding behind "Experiencing God" (based on the philosophy of Sydney Banks and the work of Dr. George Pransky) had no religious components in it at all. So, what was he doing with a woman who, to put it as politely as I can, seemed like some kind of new-age nut who talked about near-death experiences? Had Michael lost his mind?

No, it didn't seem like it. His current blogs and videos were still highly intelligent, reality-based pieces that revealed how the human mind really works. I had to know what was going on with him. So, I called him up and asked him what in the world he was doing with this Anita person.

"She's real," he said. "She's as real, straight, true, and unassuming as anyone I ever met. And her experience, what she saw, was real."

It was not only that, he said, but Anita Moorjani had found a way to tell her story (backed up and confirmed by the medical doctors who were treating her for the cancer that later caused her brain to shut down and "die") in a way that moved her audiences and readers to see life differently and live it in a fuller way.

I trusted Michael. When he talked about Anita, he was as grounded and razor-sharp as ever. Even more so. So, I had to check this out. I watched some video conversations he had with her, and I read her internationally bestselling book, *Dying to Be*

Me. I also searched around and noticed she'd been interviewed (and taken very seriously) by many mainstream entities such as CNN's Anderson Cooper 360, National Geographic International, Fox and Friends, and PBS. These journalistic entities are not known to give credence or extensive airtime to nut cases (unless you count their political coverage).

I recommend you read her book, watch her on YouTube, or get a download of Michael's program with her, because her story is absolutely riveting and almost impossible to deny.

But what most impressed Michael and me was Anita's devotion to teaching the world what her experience meant. For all of us. Especially those of us in our later years who, from time to time, may fear or dread the approach of death.

She says, "Imagine what it would be like to get up every day knowing you are and always have been perfect, complete, and inseparable from Source." That's what happened for her when her brain flatlined and she "died." So, far from losing consciousness, her consciousness expanded, left her body, encountered loving souls from her past, and in that state overheard conversations doctors and nurses were having in a closed room way down the hall from her death bed. The content of these conversations was later confirmed by the shocked medical people who were part of them.

Her experience opened the door to several questions and insights. What if consciousness was not a product of our body and brain? What if consciousness was primary, not secondary, and we, in our consciousness, identified with a body and brain only for as long as they are helpful for our earthbound adventure? In other words, what if our brains and bodies are NOT the sum total of who we are (as we almost always believe)? What if they merely fall away when their usefulness is over? (Remember our Conversation Twelve, "Your Outer Wrapper.")

What if we are spiritual beings having a human experience, for which a brain and body are required (until they aren't)? Could death then mean opening the way—or reentering—the higher realm Anita calls Source?

She says that if we could see that reality and truth for ourselves, our fear-based lives on Earth would be entirely different. We would, in her words, "Live with a soul-deep sense of self-love. Feeling completely whole and at peace with every aspect of who you are, joyously following your life purpose."

That sure sounds good, and lucky her; she had a near-death experience (NDE) that gave her full enlightenment. But what about you and me? Is that just one more proposition we must have faith in or not—until we get there?

I had that question myself, so I started exploring NDEs. I found that there were thousands of them on record, some from formerly skeptical doctors themselves, where the brain was dead and useless, but a welcoming consciousness survived. Like Anita, they were transported into a realm full of peace and love and light.

I have also studied the spiritual teachings of Christian mystics, Buddhist monks, Sufi masters, and other guides. Many advocate and even promise that enough meditation, contemplative prayer, love, and compassion for others will take you right now inside the Source or the spiritual realm that Anita experienced. Your brain and body don't have to die for you to get there. It isn't a place to get to. You're already there. You just don't see or feel it (yet).

But don't most of us claiming to be rational human beings want some scientific support for this kind of contention? Fortunately for me, I searched around and found a computer scientist and philosopher of metaphysics whose whole approach to the study of consciousness is rigorously scientific. His name is Dr. Bernardo Kastrup, and his work is deep, highly intellectual, and complex. His books aren't for everyone, but his conclusions and discoveries are.

His books and blogs and video interviews take you into how he arrived at his conclusions through the scientific method. For those interested, go to Amazon or his website www.bernardokastrup.com. His most famous (and to me most powerful) book is *Why Materialism Is Baloney: How True Skeptics Know There Is No Death and Fathom Answers to Life, the Universe and Everything.*

Note that people laughed at the discoveries of the atom and later quantum physics. We used to think of the world as made up of hard and separate material things. This turned out to be inaccurate when the world was revealed to actually be made up of pure energy swirling at different speeds to create the illusion of matter. One quantum physicist whom Alan Watts talked about began wearing snowshoes around his house so he wouldn't fall through his floor, which he'd discovered was actually made up of empty space and energy. Obviously, an absurd reaction—and probably told for the humor of it.

Kastrup's own scientific discovery, most vital to me (and perhaps to us all), is that our brains and bodies are not separate things that eventually die but are rather swirls of energy (temporarily shaped like a brain in a body). They are a part of, or rather an expression of, Universal Consciousness, which Anita experienced and described as the "Source" of everything.

Dr. Kastrup's most famous metaphor is the whirlpool. He contends that our seemingly separate, material selves are merely whirlpools in the stream of life. We can go to a river and see a whirlpool and point at it and label it as such. We can even go back tomorrow to show the "same" whirlpool to a friend. We view it as a thing, but it's not. It's an energetic whirling inside water, an expression of a larger source. And it doesn't "disappear," it just expands out into the rest of the water, dancing and swirling in another form or, more accurately, formation. It is the same for our form—our "wrapper." When it no longer serves us, it is released or reintegrated into Source, from whence it came.

The old assumption that consciousness somehow can only come from some separate material construction like a brain has never been successfully explained. There is no evidence for how and why that could happen. As a quantum physicist, what Einstein (and the prayerful and meditative spiritual devotees) have discovered about energy (or "divine spirit") not only feels better but makes more sense.

In Dr. Kastrup's book, *More Than Allegory*, he shows where the great religious and spiritual traditions have gotten this right, and where science has gotten it wrong. Even the legendary scientist and inventor Nikola Tesla said, "The day science begins to study non-physical phenomena, it will make more progress in one decade than in all the previous centuries of its existence." And compared with Tesla's time, a decade of exploration is equivalent to about ten minutes today!

So, Will, you and I have talked about fear of death and death itself in these conversations and outside of them. We both knew that the subject is potentially more front and center to older people like us because if we believe in materiality, as most people still do, we naturally assume that being older brings us closer and closer to our "demise." And that belief leads to a "What's the use?" attitude toward creating a new, better, more purpose-driven life in our later years.

We also agreed that including a chapter on surviving death would be risky and might make us look (even more) like nutcases and perhaps invalidate all the helpful and practical choices we've put into this bucket list of mindful choices. But I'm glad we compromised by agreeing to include it as our last conversation. Putting it in the front of the book might have triggered a lot of low Amazon reviews where people said, "I stopped reading after the first chapter! I don't even know what's in the second chapter—UFOs, maybe?"

People who read this book don't have to believe any of this. Trying to believe one thing or another isn't the best use of your brain. My recommendation is that you embark on whatever spiritual journey you feel compelled to follow, no matter your age. Experience for yourself, as we have, that the journey itself is worth your time and will lift your spirits and have a positive impact on this day—today, the only day any of us have to live within.

Will

Steve, thanks for agreeing to save this conversation until last. It is a way of offering something to ponder beyond the closing of this book.

In listening to you talk about NDEs, the similarities between the reports of the experiences are striking. Though it unsurprisingly reads as a bit academic, Dr. Kastrup summarized the common observations of reported NDEs[84] as follows:

- Association between a perceived light source and feelings of unconditional love, acceptance, bliss, serenity, and peace.
- The feeling of being back "Home" in the place from which one's primordial self, originated.
- Interactions with what are perceived as entities of some sort, variously described as angels, deceased relatives, or undefined, abstract "presences."
- The sensation of knowing (or rather, *remembering*) everything there is to be known about reality and one's true identity. This often includes the idea that ordinary life is a kind of dream.
- A life review and excursions across the universe that transcend linear time or space constraints, as if everything happened "here and now."
- Transcendence of all dichotomies, like good/evil, positive/negative, past/future, I/you, subject/object, etc.
- The notion there is an important purpose to ordinary life.

In comparing the reports from those who have survived death—no matter their culture, belief systems, religion, or spiritual foundation (or lack thereof)—there are undeniable common elements among them. I have seen and read many interviews of people who've reported having NDEs. Based upon viewing and reading them, I offer a plain(er) language of the commonly reported themes:

- Your body is left behind, no longer required. You are "out of body."
- You feel effortlessly lifted to a higher plain for better viewing the scenes immediately around you (as seen from "above").
- Your perspective is shifted from the earthbound to the universal.
- Existing feelings are replaced with bliss, joy, peace, and a sense of complete understanding and acceptance.
- You feel "complete," a sense of perfection as you are.
- Moving through a welcoming dark tunnel and being led to a bright but gentle white light.
- As you approach the light Source, it lifts you up and into an incredible sense of being where you should be and feeling completely safe.

I also reviewed the findings reported by Dr. Jeffrey Long, an MD and the founder of the Near-Death Experience Research Foundation (www.nderf.org). In an article entitled "Near-Death Experiences—Evidence for Their Reality," he wrote that almost all (95.6 percent) of the 1,122 NDE survivors he surveyed reported that they believed their experience was "definitely real."[85] Only one-tenth of one percent said that the incident was "definitely not real."

The NDE brings to mind the word transcendent. A transcendent experience takes you out of yourself and offers a window to a more meaningful life, one without the usual boundaries we experience.

The American writers and philosophers Ralph Waldo

Emerson, Henry David Thoreau, and Margaret Fuller, among others known as "transcendentalists," believed in the unity of all creation, the essential goodness of humankind, and the superiority of spiritual vision over logic and mere intellect. Moreover, they firmly believed in the strength and value of the individual over imitating others or being overcome with conformity. Conversation Five, "The One and Only You," was, in part, an homage to these pioneering and influential transcendentalists.

This form of transcendence—a more profound, less material life experience—opened many minds during the first half of the 19th century and impacted untold others since then, including yours and mine.

This conversation is too limited to go beyond the basics of life's spiritual nature, its omnipresence, and the opportunity to deepen our human experience by recognizing our Spirit (Light) within. There are many teachers, guides, means, and methods for greater understanding and practices to be followed, and countless ways to experience it. I will briefly mention just one such vehicle.

Meditation arrived like a tsunami during the second half of the last century. It introduced many Eastern beliefs and practices, including an emphasis on quiet, individual contemplation. Not everyone welcomed these concepts.

Even today, some people view meditation with suspicion. For some, anything that takes us away from the material—our daily challenges and well-worn routines—is questioned. Since we are offering food for further thought here, consider these observations from my own experience (and I am not a master by any means). Meditation in most forms includes:

- Reducing the noise of the outside world and its pulls and distractions.
- Getting your body in a comfortable position so that you can eliminate your physicality as a distraction.
- Quieting your body and mind and raising awareness of your breathing.
- Closing your eyes and finding a comfortable, neutral visualization as though you are gazing or staring—letting all specific images go.
- After a while, as you keep your eyes gently closed, you will discover varying shades of light, usually not bright or intense.
- Not feeling tethered to anything in particular, but being open to what passes through, even if it is simply accepting that it is okay to be at rest (in a state of "beginner's mind" or "no-mind").
- Being uplifted, positive, and self-accepting, with worries put aside naturally. Stress seems to slip away if you stay in the space you have created (physically and spiritually).

Transcending your physical senses can lead to some of the feelings commonly described by those reporting NDE experiences. Carl Jung wrote of his own near-death experience in his book, *Memories, Dreams, Reflections*,

> This experience gave me a feeling of extreme poverty, but at the same time of great fullness. There was no longer anything I wanted or desired. I existed in an objective form; I was what I had been and lived. At first

> the sense of annihilation predominated, of having been stripped or pillaged; but suddenly that became of no consequence…
>
> We shy away from the word "eternal," but I can describe the experience only as the ecstasy of a non-temporal state in which present, past, and future are one.

We bring our perspectives on life to each choice we confront, formed through filtered experiences lived as imperfect beings. We are incapable of perfect objectivity or a sense of complete meaning and spirituality. But we can get better than we are today.

Pursuing a deeper Spiritual life now could represent a prelude or preview of what transcendence will be for each of us as we let go of the materiality of body and mind. Learning to liberate our worldly selves (even for short periods) can lead to glimpses of the wonder experienced by those souls who have been beyond and back.

Mindful Choice #29

I will explore the paths of spirituality that call me and appreciate the senses of being whole, free, and loved in this life and beyond.

Closing Conversation
Devotion

Steve

I am grateful to you, Will, for coming up with the idea for this book and doing so much research and investigation into the science, statistics, and reality of aging.

I also love how you have modeled for our readers (and me) how much creative energy and *devotion* one can bring to a project—or any other choice—even when you are in the "senior" stage of physical life.

Through each topic we explore here in our 29 conversations, the common theme is myth-busting. The myths suggest, "The older your body gets, and the more your physical appearance changes—you are of lesser value, less able to make meaningful contributions, and should accept feeling less enthusiasm for life itself." Older adults can rely upon the "wisdom" of these myths to support a comfortable slide into a life on the sidelines. If you look around, you will see many who have defaulted to this choice.

But must we accept these myths, and the many others offered to us?

That's what you and I have asked about every aspect of aging we examined. And the answer is always "No"—often an *emphatic* "No!" Not only does one's love of life need not diminish and fade away in our later years, but there are plenty of fresh opportunities for it to *increase*.

This truth was so exciting to discover. And my wish is that our readers find the same excitement and encouragement that you and I found in our investigations, conversations, and the creation that is the result.

What was most poignant and inspiring in our discoveries was the word I used to describe your approach to this project, Will. The powerful and energizing concept of *devotion*. Age has no bearing on the devotion we can bring to any mindful choice we make, including the 29 we have offered for our readers' consideration. When it comes to devotion, age is irrelevant.

I'll leave you with a quotation by a wonderful author who is in her "senior" years of life yet writes like a jubilant 20-year-old. Her name is Joan Tollifson, and this passage comes from her book Death: The End of Self-Improvement.[86] She says,

> Some people think devotion means being at the feet of some guru, but it's equally possible to be devoted to the sounds of rain, the taste of tea, the aroma of coffee, the sensations throughout the body, the ways the afternoon light dances on the wall, the listening presence, the silence, the stillness beholding and permeating it all. Devotion is awake to both the beauty and the brokenness of life. It finds the extraordinary in the ordinary, the perfection in the imperfection, the miraculous in the everyday. Devotion is unconditional love and gratitude for everything.

What say you, my friend?

Will

My first reaction to what you said was, "Steve, you can't mention me personally in the conclusion!" And the second thought I had was, "It's unconventional, and more than that, I am not worthy."

But then I sat with it for a few days.

Now I say for the record, "Thank you for your very considerate and kind words. Coming from you, they mean so very much." As always, you were sending a powerful message to our readers. But unfortunately, I was too caught up in my ego and feelings of embarrassment to appreciate it right away.

Our conversations here are honest, and we have revealed much about our personal stories. You have been equally devoted to this effort *and* carrying an extra burden. You have faced some health issues that required you to weather days and weeks of being "energy-challenged." Unfortunately, I was less understanding than I could have been. Yet, you stayed the course to put these words and thoughts into the world for others who might benefit.

We have used a mainstream vocabulary for writing about change: creation, ownership, intention, commitment, renewal, transformation, self-reliance, engagement, and more. These words all apply and are appropriate in the contexts used.

But your raising of the word devotion is brilliant and timely. Devotion is "Love, loyalty, or enthusiasm for a person, activity, or cause." It is worthy of being the last "word" in our conversations as it can apply to everything from self-care of our bodies to learning and growing in Spirit. Devotion is a powerful word with a soft edge that seems better suited to the part of life's journey you and I are on now (along with 74+ million other people over 60).

We invite each of our readers to turn the focus of devotion onto themselves. To reflect "love, loyalty, and enthusiasm" in the living of your best remaining life. All of us certainly can and should "do" things, but we encourage experimentation with "being" and "becoming." These are the enduring changes we spoke about in our introductory conversation and have framed throughout the rest.

The challenges and opportunities for seniors today are much different than they were in previous generations. You now know that you can choose a LIFE RESET to deal with them on your terms. If you want it to be different, it can be different. If you want it to stay the same, it can stay the same. *Mindful choosing* is the core action.

No matter the choices made for more mindful well-being, for yourself and others, please be kind, forgiving, and loving in the process. "Rejoice and be glad in it."

"Since our lives—whether we acknowledge it or not—unfold nowhere but in transcendent space, the number of years with which we measure their duration also has no meaning. Life is about depth of experience--- how hard you love, how intensely you explore, how sincerely you express yourself—and insight—how deeply you inquire, how discerningly you ask questions. If our culture as a whole truly recognized this, the world would be a very different place."

~ Bernardo Kastrup, *More Than Allegory*

Endnotes

Conversation One: A Bucketful of Choices

[1] Will and I are both personal and business transformation coaches and authors of numerous books. We will refer to the books and coaching anecdotes from time-to-time (when we think they may have value), not as advertisements, but because they are part of our life experiences. Feel free, of course, to investigate any of them.

Conversation Two: How to Measure Life Expectancy

[2] https://www.amazon.com/Life-EXPECTANCY-Never-Late-Change/dp/0984989307/ref=tmm_pap_swatch_0?_encoding=UTF8&qid=1361560062&sr=1-2
[3] The time doesn't add up to 24 hours as these are averages and don't reflect all activities.

Conversation Three: Exploding the Mythology of Aging

[4] https://www.amazon.com/CREATOR-Steve-Chandler/dp/1600251315/ref=sr_1_1?keywords=creator+chandler&qid=1628901792&s=books&sr=1-1
[5] https://www.inc.com/heidi-zak/adults-make-more-than-35000-decisions-per-day-here-are-4-ways-to-prevent-mental-burnout.html#:~:text=It's%20estimated%20that%20the%20average,than%2035%2C000%20decisions%20per%20day
[6] https://www.amazon.com/100-Ways-Motivate-Yourself-Third/dp/1601632444/ref=sr_1_1?keywords=100+ways+chandler&qid=1628902597&s=books&sr=1-1

Conversation Six: Your Money or Your Time?

[7] https://www.amazon.com/Zen-Mind-Beginners-Informal-Meditation/dp/1590308492/ref=tmm_pap_swatch_0?_encoding=UTF8&qid=1619814749&sr=1-4

[8] Source: https://www.cbpp.org/research/social-security/social-security-lifts-more-americans-above-poverty-than-any-other-program (2019)
[9] Source: The survey upon which this conclusion was based was completed before the economic consequences of COVID-19 began to unfold in 2020. https://finance.yahoo.com/news/survey-69-americans-less-1-171927256.html https://www.gobankingrates.com/saving-money/savings-advice/americans-have-less-than-1000-in-savings/?utm_campaign=901519&utm_source=yahoo.com&utm_content=12
[10] Source: https://news.northwesternmutual.com/planning-and-progress-2019
[11] Ibid.

Conversation Eight: Letting Go to Grow

[12] https://www.investopedia.com/terms/c/creativedestruction.asp

Conversation Nine: Create the Family You Want to Have

[13] https://www.nytimes.com/2021/07/29/opinion/estranged-american-families.html?campaign_id=9&emc=edit_nn_20210730&instance_id=36631&nl=the-morning®i_id=71137299&segment_id=64861&te=1&user_id=35b257850e9ca3ae364e7d273f248909

Conversation Ten: The Search for a Senior "Match"

[14] Rainer Maria Rilke, *Correspondence* (March 1907)
[15] https://www.ingentaconnect.com/content/sbp/sbp/2004/00000032/00000002/art00007
[16] http://psychology.iresearchnet.com/social-psychology/interpersonal-relationships/companionate-love/ and https://www.theatlantic.com/family/archive/2021/02/falling-in-love-wont-make-you-happy/617989/
[17] Agape is referenced in the New Testament and refers to a love not of emotions or feelings but of the will and of choice. It is an ongoing commitment to what is good for another.

Conversation Eleven: Tapping Your Full Potential

[18] https://hbr.org/2021/05/research-what-do-people-need-to-perform-at-a-high-level?utm_medium=email&utm_source=newsletter_weekly&utm_campaign=insider_activesubs&utm_content=signinnudge&deliveryName=DM133414

Conversation Thirteen: Normal Aging—Everything is Connected

[19] https://www.webmd.com/healthy-aging/guide/normal-aging#1 and https://www.cdc.gov/aging/publications/features/dementia-not-normal-aging.html#:~:text=What%20is%20Normal%20Aging%3F&text=Heart%20and%20blood%20vessels%3A%20Stiffening,fragile%20and%20likely%20to%20break.
[20] Almost everyone will confront some or all these changes. They may arise earlier or later in life depending upon the individual. Many factors come into play, including but not limited to genetic composition, personal physical care, avoidance of chronic diseases, accidents, and other variables. To learn more, ask your doctor or another health professional.
[21] https://www.merriam-webster.com/dictionary/health%20span
[22]
https://www.amazon.com/dp/0578855038/ref=sr_1_1?dchild=1&keywords=untethered+aging&qid=1615995500&sr=8-1
[23] https://www.theatlantic.com/science/archive/2019/09/how-brain-helps-you-pay-attention/598846/

Conversation Fourteen: Our Bodies Want to Be Well

[24] https://www.healthaffairs.org/doi/full/10.1377/hlthaff.2017.0767 Interestingly, over the past 50 years improvements in the U.S. infant mortality rate have not kept pace with other major countries.
[25] https://www.nature.com/articles/s42003-019-0290-0/figures/1 In this chart, CHF means congestive heart failure. COPD means chronic obstructive pulmonary disease (a chronic inflammatory lung disease that causes obstructed airflow from the lungs). MI is myocardial infarction, commonly known as a heart attack. Healthspan means the number of years of living in a relatively disease-free state.
[26] Koh HK, Parekh AK, Park JJ. Confronting the Rise and Fall of US Life Expectancy. JAMA. 2019;322(20):1963–1965. doi:10.1001/jama.2019.17303
[27] https://www.washingtonpost.com/health/theres-something-terribly-wrong-americans-are-dying-young-at-alarming-rates/2019/11/25/d88b28ec-0d6a-11ea-8397-a955cd542d00_story.html
[28] https://messaging-custom-newsletters.nytimes.com/template/oakv2?abVariantId=0&campaign_id=9&emc=edit_nn_20210722&instance_id=35950&nl=the-morning&productCode=NN®i_id=71137299&segment_id=64106&te=1&uri=nyt%3A%2F%2Fnewsletter%2F704adac3-9635-52bb-8d26-4e8664ddba2d&user_id=35b257850e9ca3ae364e7d273f248909

[29] Drug overdoses, suicides, and alcohol-related liver mortality. *Mortality and Morbidity in the 21st Century*, Case and Deaton, https://www.brookings.edu/wp-content/uploads/2017/08/casetextsp17bpea.pdf
[30] https://www.bmj.com/content/362/bmj.k2817
[31] https://www.nytimes.com/interactive/2021/07/14/upshot/drug-overdose-deaths.html?campaign_id=29&emc=edit_up_20210715&instance_id=35400&nl=the-
upshot®i_id=71137299&segment_id=63543&te=1&user_id=35b257850e9ca3ae364e7d273f248909
[32] https://www.cigna.com/about-us/newsroom/studies-and-reports/loneliness-epidemic-america

Conversation Fifteen: The Pain of Gain

[33] https://www.infoplease.com/world/health-statistics/fattest-countries-world
[34] https://www.nejm.org/doi/full/10.1056/NEJMsa1909301
[35] https://www.brookings.edu/bpea-articles/mortality-and-morbidity-in-the-21st-century/ and https://www.washingtonpost.com/national/health-science/new-research-identifies-a-sea-of-despair-among-white-working-class-americans/2017/03/22/c777ab6e-0da6-11e7-9b0d-d27c98455440_story.html
[36] Daily energy expenditure through the human life course https://science.sciencemag.org/content/373/6556/808/tab-pdf
[37] The scientists said that while the metabolic rate patterns hold for the population, individuals vary. But the outliers do not change the general pattern reflected in graphs showing the trajectory of metabolic rates over the years.
[38] *What We Think We Know About Metabolism May Be Wrong* https://www.nytimes.com/2021/08/12/health/metabolism-weight-aging.html
[39] http://www.shieldhealthcare.com/community/news/2012/07/10/nutrition-over-70-a-guide-to-senior-dietary-needs/
[40] Emily J. McAllister, and others, (2009) Ten Putative Contributors to the Obesity Epidemic, Critical Reviews in Food Science and Nutrition, 49:10, 868-913, DOI: 10.1080/10408390903372599
[41] https://www.eatthis.com/unhealthiest-fast-food/
[42] Here are the Top 25 fast food items by calories compiled by USA Today: https://www.usatoday.com/story/money/2019/07/18/sonic-burger-king-popeyes-fast-food-items-with-most-calories/39685391/
[43] Emily J. McAllister, and others, (2009) "Ten Putative Contributors to the Obesity Epidemic," Critical Reviews in Food Science and Nutrition, 49:10, 868-913, DOI: 10.1080/10408390903372599

Conversation Sixteen: I'm Walkin', Yes Indeed

[44] Emily J. McAllister, and others, (2009) "Ten Putative Contributors to the Obesity Epidemic," Critical Reviews in Food Science and Nutrition, 49:10, 868-913, DOI: 10.1080/10408390903372599
[45] https://deadspin.com/an-ex-cons-guide-to-prison-weightlifting-1571930353
[46] https://www.nih.gov/news-events/nih-research-matters/number-steps-day-more-important-step-intensity
[47] Your core from your torso down to your hips. Your core provides a muscular framework that protects your internal organs, aids movement, and provides balance and stability to your whole body. A well-known core exercise is sit-ups.

Conversation Nineteen: Refuse to be Ushered Offstage

[48] https://www.healthline.com/health/benefits-of-singing#benefits
[49] https://www.nytimes.com/interactive/2021/04/08/magazine/skagit-valley-chorale-COVID-superspreader.html
[50] You can listen to their 2020 online concert on YouTube (with everyone singing in separate locations) and feel for yourself the beauty and heart of their singing. https://www.youtube.com/watch?v=bqYdNIk5fug

Conversation Twenty: An Old Dog *Can* Learn

[51] For much more on neuroplasticity, please see, Fuchs, Eberhard, and Gabriele Flügge. "Adult neuroplasticity: more than 40 years of research." *Neural plasticity* vol. 2014 (2014): 541870. doi:10.1155/2014/541870 and Lillard, Angeline S, and Alev Erisir. "Old Dogs Learning New Tricks: Neuroplasticity Beyond the Juvenile Period." *Developmental Review: DR* vol. 31,4 (2011): 207-239. doi:10.1016/j.dr.2011.07.008
[52] The phrase "you can't teach an old dog new tricks" was originated by Heywood in 1546 and is considered one of the oldest idioms of the English language.
[53] https://dogdiscoveries.com/curiosity/neuroplasticity-of-a-dogs-brain
[54] Lally, P., van Jaarsveld, C.H.M., Potts, H.W.W. and Wardle, J. (2010), How are habits formed: Modelling habit formation in the real world. Eur. J. Soc. Psychol., 40: 998-1009. https://doi.org/10.1002/ejsp.674
[55] https://www.brainhq.com/brain-resources/brain-plasticity/what-is-brain-plasticity/
[56] https://www.forbes.com/sites/taraswart/2018/03/27/the-4-underlying-principles-to-changing-your-brain/?sh=46a6ca6b5a71
[57] Ibid.

[58] Ibid.
[59] https://www.ausmed.com/cpd/articles/exercise-induced-neuroplasticity
[60] https://gumc.georgetown.edu/news-release/key-mental-abilities-can-actually-improve-during-aging/# and https://www.nature.com/articles/s41562-021-01169-7
[61] Credit songwriter: John Deacon, Another One Bites the Dust lyrics © Queen Music Limited

Conversation Twenty-One: The (Not So Secret) Secret to Financial Sufficiency

[62] https://www.pewsocialtrends.org/2019/12/11/most-americans-say-the-current-economy-is-helping-the-rich-hurting-the-poor-and-middle-class/

Conversation Twenty-Two: The Answers to Everything

[63] https://www.statista.com/statistics/216573/worldwide-market-share-of-search-engines/
[64] https://www.pewresearch.org/fact-tank/2021/04/02/7-of-americans-dont-use-the-internet-who-are-they/
[65] Here is what Google says about How to Search on Google https://support.google.com/websearch/answer/134479?hl=en
[66] A faster way to use Google is to enter a search into the search box that's built into most popular browsers. Google's is called Chrome, Microsoft's Internet Explorer, Apple's Safari, and Mozilla's Firefox. These are available for free. If you need help, you can ask someone you know who has a smartphone.
[67] Jefferson City, MO.

Conversation Twenty-Three: We Should All Be Coaching Someone

[68] The Neuroscience of Everybody's Favorite Topic - Why do people spend so much time talking about themselves? https://www.scientificamerican.com/article/the-neuroscience-of-everybody-favorite-topic-themselves/

Conversation Twenty-Four: The Joy in Pursuing Self-Transformation

[69] In his seminal paper about human motivation, Maslow discussed self-actualization by stating, "*What a man can be, he must be. This need we may call* self-actualization" A. H. Maslow (1943) Originally published in Psychological Review, 50, 370-396. https://psychclassics.yorku.ca/Maslow/motivation.htm

[70] McLeod, S. A. (2020, March 20). *Maslow's hierarchy of needs*. Simply Psychology. https://www.simplypsychology.org/maslow.html 1. They perceive reality efficiently and can tolerate uncertainty; 2. Accept themselves and others for what they are; 3. Spontaneous in thought and action; 4. Problem-centered (not self-centered); 5. Unusual sense of humor; 6. Able to look at life objectively; 7. Highly creative; 8. Resistant to enculturation, but not purposely unconventional; 9. Concerned for the welfare of humanity; 10. Capable of deep appreciation of basic life-experience; 11. Establish deeply satisfying interpersonal relationships with a few people; 12. Peak experiences; 13. Need for privacy; 14. Democratic attitudes; and 15. Strong moral/ethical standards.
[71] https://blogs.scientificamerican.com/beautiful-minds/what-does-it-mean-to-be-self-actualized-in-the-21st-century/
[72] Wade GH. A concept analysis of personal transformation. J Adv Nurs. 1998 Oct;28(4):713-9. doi: 10.1046/j.1365-2648.1998.00729.x. PMID: 9829658 https://pubmed.ncbi.nlm.nih.gov/9829658/

Conversation Twenty-Five: Passion: Fuel for Living

[73] Vallerand, R.J. The role of passion in sustainable psychological well-being. *Psych Well-Being* **2,** 1 (2012). https://doi.org/10.1186/2211-1522-2-1
[74] Ibid.
[75] Ibid.
[76] Ibid.

Conversation Twenty-Six: Let Nature Fill You Up

[77] https://www.nytimes.com/2021/04/24/opinion/nomadland-oscars.html?action=click&module=RelatedLinks&pgtype=Article
[78] https://www.cntraveller.com/gallery/nomadland-where-was-it-filmed
[79] https://www.imdb.com/title/tt9770150/characters/nm10470534; and https://medium.com/illumination/sailboats-and-swallows-loss-grief-and-meaning-in-nomadland-695f11a2b9ce
[80] https://www.washingtonpost.com/lifestyle/home/poets-and-gardening-louise-gluck/2020/12/15/0737ef0a-3a50-11eb-98c4-25dc9f4987e8_story.html

Conversation Twenty-Seven: This Is the Day the Lord Has Made

[81] Psalms 118:24 "This is the day which the Lord hath made; we will rejoice and be glad in it."

[82] https://www.youtube.com/watch?v=xr6VawX2nr4
[83] www.anitamoorjani.com

Conversation Twenty-Nine: Surviving Death

[84] https://www.bernardokastrup.com/2012/03/ndes-and-after-life-reality.html
[85] https://www.ncbi.nlm.nih.gov/pmc/articles/PMC6172100/#b1-ms111_p0372
Copyright 2014 by the Missouri State Medical Association

Closing Conversation: Devotion

[86] https://www.amazon.com/Death-End-Self-Improvement-Joan-Tollifson/dp/1916290302

Our Gratitude

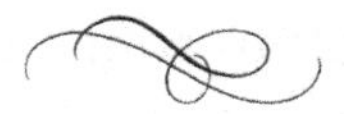

Steve

Heartfelt thanks to my own life and business coach Steve Hardison without whose guidance and love I would not be who or where I am today and certainly not be seeing my aging and senior years as opportunities for joy and creativity.

To the many other teachers, mentors, and sources of inspiration whose works and teaching have lifted me: Byron Katie, Nathaniel Branden, Werner Erhard, Ken Wilber, Drs Ron, and Mary Hulnick, Ellen Emmet, Dr. Ron Howard, Dicken Bettinger, and Francis Lucille among others.

To Kathy, for love and support beyond words.

To Chris Nelson, Kathy Eimers, and Brannan Sirratt for their expert editorial guidance, and Carrie Brito for her cover contributions.

And especially to my dear friend Will Keiper, who was the inspiring, driving, force behind the content for this book. It was a sheer delight and an honor to be his co-author.

Will

To my coach, muse, and friend, it was an honor to co-create this book of conversations with you, Steve. Thank you for putting up with my impatience and sometimes obsessive "need for speed," and taking it with good humor.

With gratitude for the wisdom imparted by the American transcendentalists, Ralph Waldo Emerson, Henry David Thoreau, Margaret Fuller, Walt Whitman, and their contemporaries. Their thinking and words have shaped my view of the world and my work in transcendence in the 21st century. I wish I could have walked with them in this Earthly domain.

Many other thinkers and philosophers have helped expand my intellectual pursuits through their thought-provoking approaches and work. Carl Jung, Werner Erhard, Albert Ellis, Maxie Maultsby, Jr., Abraham Maslow, Friedrich Nietzsche, and Viktor Frankl, among many.

With appreciation for the guidance and truth of our editing professionals, Chris Nelson, Kathy Eimers, Brannan Sirratt, and Carrie Brito.

Recommended Reading

Taking Responsibility: Self-Reliance and the Accountable Life by Nathaniel Branden

Learned Optimism: How to Change Your Mind and Your Life by Martin E. P. Seligman

Loving What Is: Four Questions That Can Change Your Life by Byron Katie and Stephen Mitchell

Dying to Be Me: My Journey from Cancer, to Near Death, to True Healing by Anita Moorjani

The Inside-Out Revolution: The Only Thing You Need to Know to Change Your Life Forever by Michael Neill

Happiness: A Guide to Developing Life's Most Important Skill by Matthieu Ricard

Remembering the Light Within by Drs. Ron and Mary Hulnick

Zen Mind, Beginner's Mind by Shunryu Suzuki

The Power of Intention: Learning to Co-Create Your World Your Way by Wayne Dyer

If You Want to Write by Brenda Ueland

Why Materialism Is Baloney by Bernardo Kastrup

The Untethered Soul by Michael Singer

Ralph Waldo Emerson's Self-Reliance, Translated by Adam Khan

Death: The End of Self-Improvement by Joan Tollifson

The Fear of Insignificance by Carlo Strenger

In Search of Wisdom by Matthieu Ricard et al.

Man's Search for Meaning by Viktor Frankl

Eternity Now by Francis Lucille

Deep Work: Rules for Focused Success in a Distracted World by Cal Newport

Coming Home: Uncovering the Foundations of Psychological Well-Being by Dicken Bettinger and Natasha Swerdloff

The Well-Gardened Mind: The Restorative Power of Nature by Sue Stuart-Smith

The Inner Work of Aging: Shifting From Role to Soul by Connie Zweig, Ph.D.

Songs Referenced

"Old Man Mose" by Louis Armstrong

"Take Me to the River" by Foghat

"One Man's Pleasure" by Molly Hatchet

"I Ain't Got Nobody" by Leon Redbone

"Young at Heart" by Frank Sinatra

"Stayin' Alive" by the Bee Gees

"I'm Walkin'" by Fats Domino

"Another One Bites the Dust" by Queen

"This Is the Day the Lord Has Made" by Fred Hammond

"My Way" by Frank Sinatra

All referenced songs can be accessed on youtube.com using the song title and the artist's name.

About the Authors

Steve Chandler is the author and co-author of more than 35 books, including the bestsellers *Time Warrior*, *Reinventing Yourself*, *100 Ways to Motivate Yourself*, and *The Prosperous Coach*.

He has been a seminar leader, sales and leadership trainer, business, and success coach for more than 30 years. He is the founder and lead teacher in the internationally respected Coaching Prosperity School. His latest book is *How to Get Clients – New Pathways to Coaching Prosperity*.

He lives with his family in Birmingham, Michigan, and can be reached through his website:

www.stevechandler.com

William (Will) Keiper is a business advisor, coach, and expert in conquering the challenges of transitions. He is an award-winning nonfiction author, having written *Untethered Aging*, *Life Expectancy – It's Never Too Late to Change Your Game*, *The Power of Urgency*, and *Cyber Crisis – It's Personal Now*, among others.

He has been a NYSE, NASDAQ, and private company CEO. He is recognized as a pragmatic truth-teller and change agent when speed and urgency matter. He is committed to helping humans and businesses desiring transformation to do things differently by seeing things differently.

He can be reached through his website at:

www.williamkeiper.com

Made in the USA
Monee, IL
11 October 2021

79833014R00154